Essays in
Biochemistry

D1363902

Essays in Biochemistry

Edited for The Biochemical Society by

P. N. Campbell

Courtauld Institute of Biochemistry
The Middlesex Hospital
Medical School
London W1P 7PN
England

W. N. Aldridge

MRC Toxicology Unit
Woodmansterne Road
Carshalton
Surrey SM5 4EF
England

Volume 14

1978

Published for The Biochemical Society by Academic Press
London, New York and San Francisco

ACADEMIC PRESS INC. (LONDON) LTD
24/28 Oval Road
London NW1

U.S. Edition published by
ACADEMIC PRESS INC.
111 Fifth Avenue
New York
New York 10003

Library of Congress Catalog Card Number 65 15522
ISBN 0 12 158114 4

Printed in Great Britain by
Spottiswoode Ballantyne Ltd.
Colchester and London

Biography

John Kenny after graduating in Medicine from London University, spent several years in clinical posts before deciding to learn something about research in more basic medical sciences. This opportunity arose in the Department of Pharmacology at Johns Hopkins University where he began to investigate the inactivation of glucagon by various tissues. He returned to the U.K. to continue studies on the degradation of peptide hormones and took his Ph.D in Biochemistry at the University of Cambridge. In 1958, he was appointed to the staff at Leeds, where he concentrated his research on tissue peptidases. His interest in the kidney brush border followed naturally on finding that an endopeptidase was localized in this membrane. His present research is directed towards an understanding of the organization and function of the proteins of the brush border membrane.

Andrew G. Booth graduated from the University of Leeds and received his Ph.D in 1975. He has been working with John Kenny for the last six years and has recently been appointed to a Temporary Lectureship in the Department of Biochemistry at Leeds. He is interested in the structure of microvilli with particular emphasis on the role of the contractile proteins in pinocytosis.

Brian T. Pickering graduated in Biological Chemistry at the University of Bristol in 1958 and received his Ph.D in 1961. After periods in the University of California and the National Institute for Medical Research, he returned to Bristol, first in Pharmacology and then as Reader in Anatomy and Biochemistry. He is currently Professor of Anatomy. His research interests have centred around the biochemistry of pituitary polypeptides, both from a comparative point of view and, latterly, with regard to their biosynthesis and intracellular transport.

Jonathan Arch developed his interest in adenosine in Eric Newsholme's Laboratory in Oxford. In 1974, he joined Beecham Pharmaceuticals Research Division in Surrey, where he is now senior biologist in a project on obesity. His interests include the control of cyclic AMP and adenosine metabolism and the regulation of metabolic rate.

Eric A. Newsholme graduated in Natural Sciences at Cambridge. After proceeding to the degree of Ph.D of that University in 1963, he joined the MRC Unit for Research in Cell Metabolism under the direction of Professor Sir Hans Krebs, F.R.S. of Oxford. He moved to the Department of Zoology,

Oxford University, in 1967 to join the ARC Unit of Insect Physiology under the direction of Professor J. W. S. Pringle, F.R.S. He is now University Lecturer in Biochemistry, Oxford University and Fellow of Merton College. His research interests are in the field of metabolic control.

Preface

In recent volumes there has been no Preface but on this occasion when I say good-bye to my fellow editor Norman Aldridge and welcome a new colleague, Robin Marshall, an exception is being made. I am grateful to Norman Aldridge for his help since Frank Dickens retired; the only reason for the change is that he wants to devote more time to his flourishing research group. Robin Marshall has had much experience with the *Biochemical Journal* and I know will bring many new ideas as well as editorial experience.

While attending the 12th meeting of FEBS in Dresden a lady from Czechoslovakia asked me why biochemists were interested only in the *lac* operon. In the moments before my reply I felt like a tennis player poised to return an easy lob yet anxious lest he knock the ball out of court. In truth my reply was not difficult for one only has to look at the subjects under discussion at a FEBS meeting to see that biochemists are concerned with a wide variety of biological phenomena. We have tried to reflect this approach in this series and the present volume is no exception. In this way the essays may encourage others to extend their field of interest. We are always interested in suggestions for new subjects for Essays even if no author is immediately in sight.

The Publications Board of the Biochemical Society has discussed ways in which the subject matter of the Essays may be made more attractive to the general reader. As Editors we try to ensure that the published Essay is in a form acceptable to the non-expert. However there is an inherent problem because biochemists have accepted the challenge of explaining in molecular terms the complexity of biological phenomena.

There are difficulties in promoting sales of a publication of this nature, one of them resulting from attempts to keep the price per volume as low as possible. In fact it has only doubled over the 14 years of the series, so that for salesmen Essays may not appear to be an attractive proposition. It is for this reason that I have always welcomed the initiative of the Biochemical Society in providing Essays direct from their distribution centre in Colchester. Perhaps your local biochemical society would like to arrange a bulk order and would be prepared to cooperate in distribution to its members. The Editors would be pleased to hear of such proposals.

Suggestions and criticisms from any reader on any matter concerning the Essays are always welcome.

September 1978   P. N. CAMPBELL

Conventions

The abbreviations, conventions and symbols used in these Essays are those specified by the Editorial Board of *The Biochemical Journal* in *Policy of the Journal and Instructions to Authors* (revised 1976 *Biochem J.* **153**, 1–21 and amended 1978 *Biochem J.* **169**, 1–27). The following abbreviations of compounds, etc., are allowed without definition in the text.

ADP, CDP, GDP, IDP, UDP, XDP, dTDP: 5′-pyrophosphates of adenosine, cytidine, guanosine, inosine, uridine, xanthosine and thymidine

AMP, etc.: adenosine 5′-phosphate, etc.

ATP, etc.: adenosine 5′-triphosphate, etc.

CM-cellulose: carboxymethylcellulose

CoA and acyl-CoA: coenzyme A and its acyl derivatives

Cyclic AMP etc.: adenosine 3′:5′-cyclic phosphate etc.

DEAE-cellulose: diethylaminoethylcellulose

DNA: deoxyribonucleic acid

Dnp-: 2,4-dinitrophenyl-

Dns-: 5-dimethylaminonaphthalene-1-sulphonyl-

EDTA: ethylenediaminetetra-acetate

FAD: flavin-adenine dinucleotide

FMN: flavin mononucleotide

GSH, GSSG: glutathione, reduced and oxidized

NAD: nicotinamide-adenine dinucleotide

NADP: nicotinamide-adenine dinucleotide phosphate

NMN: nicotinamide mononucleotide

P_i, PP_i: orthophosphate, pyrophosphate

RNA: ribonucleic acid (see overleaf)

TEAE-cellulose: triethylaminoethylcellulose

tris: 2-amino-2-hydroxymethylpropane-1,3-diol

The combination NAD^+, NADH is preferred.

The following abbreviations for amino acids and sugars, for use only in presenting sequences and in Tables and Figures, are also allowed without definition.

Amino acids

Ala: alanine	Asx: aspartic acid or	Cys or Cys: Cystine (half)
Arg: arginine	asparagine (undefined)	
Asn*: asparagine	Cys: Cysteine	Gln†: glutamine
Asp: aspartic acid		Glu: glutamic acid

* Alternative, Asp(NH₂)   † Alternative, Glu(NH₂)

Glx: glutamic acid or
   glutamine (undefined)
Gly: glycine
His: histidine
Hyl: hydroxylysine
Hyp: hydroxyproline

Ile: isoleucine
Leu: leucine
Lys: lysine
Met: methionine
Orn: ornithine
Phe: phenylalanine

Pro: proline
Ser: serine
Thr: threonine
Trp: tryptophan
Tyr: tyrosine
Val: valine

Sugars

Ara: arabinose
dRib: 2-deoxyribose
Fru: fructose
Fuc: fucose
Gal: galactose

Glc*: glucose
Man: mannose
Rib: ribose
Xyl: xylose

* Where unambiguous, G may be used.

Abbreviations for nucleic acid used in these essays are:

mRNA: messenger RNA
nRNA: nuclear RNA
rRNA: ribosomal RNA
tRNA: transfer RNA

Other abbreviations are given on the first page of the text.

References are given in the form used in *The Biochemical Journal*, the last as well as the first page of each article being cited and, in addition, the title. Titles of journals are abbreviated in accordance with the system employed in the *Chemical Abstracts Service Source Index* (1969) and its Quarterly Supplement (American Chemical Society).

Enzyme Nomenclature

At the first mention of each enzyme in each Essay there is given, whenever possible, the number assigned to it in *Enzyme Nomenclature: Recommendations (1972) of the International Union of Biochemistry on the Nomenclature and Classification of Enzymes, together with their Units and the Symbols of Enzyme Kinetics*, Elsevier Publishing Co., Amsterdam, London and New York, 1973: this document also appeared earlier as Vol. 13 (2nd edn, 1965) of *Comprehensive Biochemistry*, (Florkin, M. & Stotz, E. H., eds), Elsevier Publishing Co., Amsterdam, London and New York. Enzyme numbers are given in the form EC 1.2.3.4. The names used by authors of the Essays are not necessarily those recommended by the International Union of Biochemistry.

Contents

Microvilli: Their Ultrastructure, Enzymology and Molecular Organization

A. J. KENNY and A. G. BOOTH

Department of Biochemistry, University of Leeds, 9, Hyde Terrace, Leeds LS2 9LS, England

I. Introduction

Microvilli are cylindrical projections of the plasma membrane about $0\cdot1$ μm in diameter, 1 to 2 μm in length, and are a common occurrence on the surface of mammalian cells. Whenever a cell surface is not in contact with another cell, but instead abuts on to a fluid-filled space, such as the lumen of the gut, or kidney tubule, the duct of a gland, the air space in the respiratory system or

1

Fig. 1. Tracheal epithelium. (a) Section through luminal membrane (rat); (b) freeze-etched preparation (guinea-pig) (from reference 132). This membrane demonstrates the differences in structure between cilia (Cil) and microvilli (Mv). (ZO, zona occludens.) Bar = 1 μm.

indeed any extracellular space, microvilli are generally to be found. If the reader doubts this statement, reference to a work on ultrastructural histology, such as Rhodin's *Histology, a Text and Atlas*,[1] will show how wide is the range of cell types with microvilli on part of their surfaces. It is useful to distinguish two structural components in each microvillus—a membrane, continuous with the plasma membrane, and a core, continuous with the cytoplasm. The core proteins determine the form of the microvillus conferring on it both stability and rigidity. The membrane has its own complement of proteins, many of them glycoproteins with hydrolase activity, the number and nature of which depend on the cell type. This general description might seem equally applicable to cilia, but it is important at the outset to realize that microvilli and cilia are not variations of the same structure. The differences between the two structures are well seen in electron micrographs of a cell, such as that of the tracheal epithelium (Fig. 1), which bears both microvilli and cilia on the same surface. Microvilli

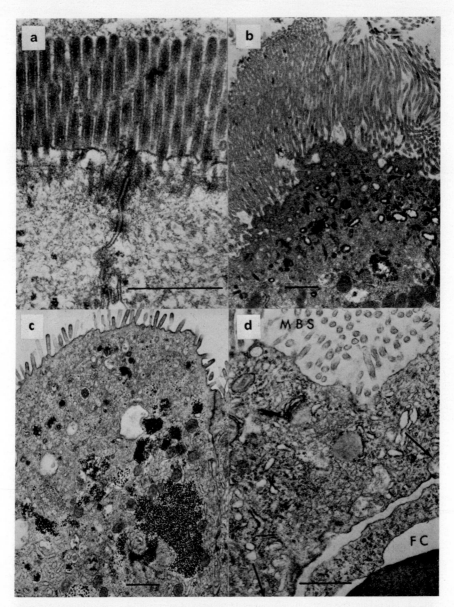

Fig. 2. Brush borders. The examples shown are (a) intestinal epithelium (rat); (b) kidney proximal tubule cell (rabbit); (c) yolk sac epithelium (rat); (d) syncytiotrophoblast from guinea-pig placenta (from reference 136) MBS, maternal blood space; arrows, infolding of basal membrane; FC, fetal capillary. Each tissue reveals a dense and regular array of microvilli on the apical surface of the cell. Bar = 1 μm.

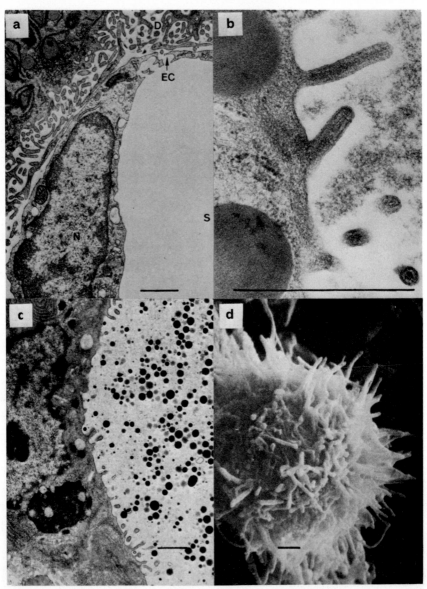

Fig. 3. Microvilli. The relatively infrequent occurrence of microvilli in these cell types contrasts with the ordered array seen in brush borders (Fig. 2). Nevertheless the ultrastructural details of microvilli are maintained in all the examples shown. (a) Liver (rat), the microvilli line the perisinusoidal space of Disse (D); S, sinusoidal space; EC, transendothelial channel; N, nucleus of endothelial cell (from reference 133). (b) Pancreas (rabbit), microvilli project into the lumen of the acinus. (c) Mammary gland (mouse). (d) Cultured lymphoid cell—a scanning electron micrograph showing a mesh of irregular and often branched microvilli (from reference 134).

are smaller than cilia and are devoid of the microtubules that are the prominent feature of the latter. An excellent review by Satir[2] of the ultrastructural aspects of these two organelles has recently appeared.

Although all microvilli are generally similar in their basic structure they vary, in different cell types, both in respect to their length and their frequency on the cell surface. When microvilli are densely packed and in a uniform array, the cell surface is described as a brush border. Other brush borders are present on the epithelial cells of the yolk sac and in syncytiotrophoblast. These four types are shown in Fig. 2.

Brush borders represent a very high degree of specialization of the plasma membrane. The lesser degrees of specialization can be seen on exposed surfaces of many other cell types—a group of these, pancreas, liver, mammary gland and a cultured lymphoid cell are shown in Fig. 3: each revealing the presence of microvilli.

II. Methods of Preparing Brush Border and Microvillus Fractions

Under appropriate conditions the apical membrane of brush border-bearing cells survives homogenization as an intact structure: the membrane tends to round up, so that such brush borders resemble bristly rosettes, usually about 10 μm diameter. Using different techniques, microvilli may shear off the apical membrane and may be purified from such suspensions in the form of microvilli. The latter preparation usually demands more vigorous homogenization than would be appropriate for brush borders. Electron micrographs of the two types of preparation are shown in Fig. 4.

A. BRUSH BORDERS

Brush borders were first prepared from hamster intestine by Miller & Crane[3] in 1961. The hamster has less intestinal mucus than many other species, a characteristic that obviates difficulties associated with the removal of this contaminant. EDTA is very commonly used in the homogenizing medium: it serves to dissociate desmosomes, so that each brush border derives from a single enterocyte. There are now a variety of different methods applicable to the intestinal mucosa, but perhaps the commonest in use is that described in 1968 by Forstner et al.,[4] which is suitable for rat intestine. The mucosal scrapings are homogenized in a medium containing 5 mM EDTA. Brush borders are sedimented at low speeds; the mucus is aggregated by addition of NaCl and the purified brush borders are obtained after filtration through glass wool. A method applicable to the preparation of kidney brush borders followed a little later (Thuneberg & Rostgaard[5]). This and all the later procedures are more complicated and more time-consuming than those for the intestine. It is

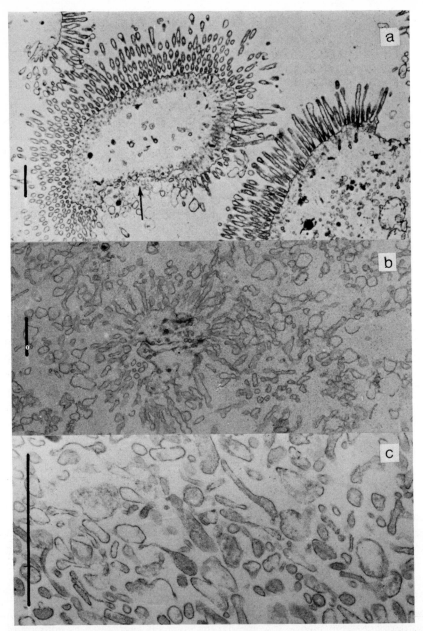

Fig. 4. Purified preparations of (a) intestinal brush borders (rat) (from reference 127); (b) kidney brush borders (rabbit); (c) kidney microvilli (rabbit). Unless special care is taken to avoid exposure to temperatures above 0°C during the fractionation, the microvilli begin to vesiculate. Indeed if the preparation is incubated at 37°C all the microvilli are converted into osmotically sensitive spherical vesicles. Bar = 1 μm.

essential that the kidney cortical tissue is disrupted by very gentle means, e.g. by extruding the tissue through a wire mesh[6] or by a loose-fitting Dounce homogenizer.[7] EDTA is rarely used and this may explain why kidney brush borders are often derived from two or more adjacent cells. A commonly used method is that of Wilfong & Neville.[7] Kidney cortex is homogenized in a large volume of hypotonic medium, from which brush borders can be sedimented at low speeds. Purification is achieved by two gradient centrifugations: one during which the brush borders float upwards and the other a rate-zonal step. Recently this same method has been successfully used to prepare brush borders from syncytiotrophoblast.[8]

B. MICROVILLI

Free microvilli, which are readily generated by more vigorous homogenization, sediment in the ultracentrifuge with a heavy microsomal pellet. Early attempts to resolve microvilli from other microsomal components were unsuccessful. The solution to this problem lay in the use of divalent cations, Ca^{2+} or Mg^{2+}, to preferentially aggregate these other components, which then sediment more rapidly than microvilli. Methods have been described for intestinal microvilli[9,10] and kidney microvilli,[11] the latter being a rapid method requiring only four differential centrifugation steps. Microvilli prepared by these methods appear to be closed right-side-out vesicles and ideally suited for transport studies.[12,13]

A wholly different approach has also had some success. It depends on the ability of the plasma membrane of intact cells to bud off small vesicles when incubated in iso- or hypo-osmolar media. Methods have been described for kidney,[14] rabbit yolk sac[15] and syncytiotrophoblast.[16] The mechanism by which these vesicles are generated is not well understood and the yields are low. However, the method may have the advantage in producing homogeneous preparations since only the plasma membrane is involved in the generation of the vesicles.

III. Ultrastructure of the Microvillus

A. THE CORE

The integrity of the microvillar interior is fundamental. The presence of a skeleton of ordered microfilaments determines the existence of a microvillus; without this support such extensions of the plasma membrane would be highly unstable. The number of microfilaments in each microvillus is a characteristic of cell type. In the kidney, seven filaments are generally present but in the intestine there are about four times as many (Fig. 5a,b). In both cases the

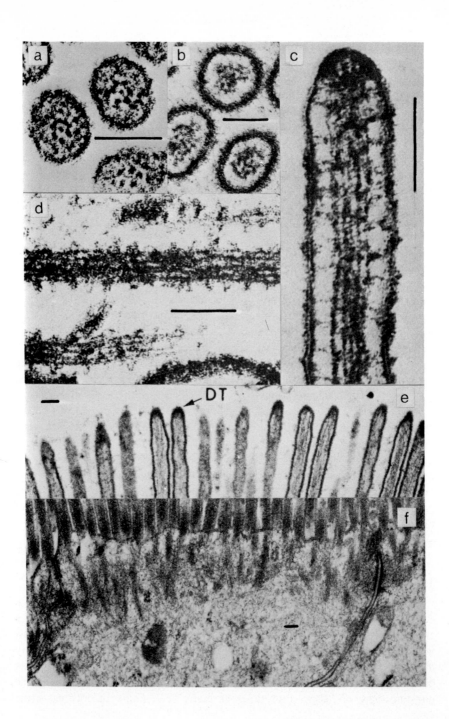

filaments are in a hexagonal array. This symmetry must imply an interaction between the microfilaments, the stability of the microvillus depending on an interaction between filaments and membrane. Lateral strands, observed by Millington & Finean,[17] seem to fulfil the latter requirement, and Mukherjee & Staehelin[18] found cross filaments that linked the microfilaments. The details of the core structure are not easily seen unless the microvillar organization has been artificially disturbed. Microvilli readily vesiculate *in vitro* by a process that is not primarily osmotic[19] and, during this change, both the micro-filaments and cross-bridges are clearly revealed. Alternatively, treatment with Mg^{2+} alters the arrangement of the microfilaments so as to reveal the cross-bridges[20] (Fig. 2c). Another way of demonstrating the ultrastructure of the core is to remove the membrane elements by treatment with a non-ionic detergent. The core proteins are not solubilized by this treatment and the cross-bridges can be seen protruding perpendicularly from the microfilaments (Fig. 5d) with a periodicity of about 30–40 nm.[20] At the microvillar tip a further structural feature relating the core to the membrane can be seen in electron micrographs. There is some electron-dense material (Fig. 5e), which also persists after treatment with detergent. At the base of each microvillus the microfilaments extend from the core into the apical region of the cell—a zone referred to as the terminal web. Here they mingle with other filaments (intermediate or tonofilaments) arising from the desmosomal complex that encircles the cell just below the apical region (Fig. 5f).

B. THE MEMBRANE

In thin sections a typical trilaminar membrane, 8–10 nm in thickness, can be seen. The existence of a lipid bilayer has been confirmed by X-ray diffraction.[21] In the intestine thin sections of the brush border frequently reveal a poly-saccharide coat (Fig. 6a) referred to as the glycocalyx or "fuzz". It is especially marked at the tips of microvilli. Special staining methods using cationic colloids, e.g. ruthenium red, colloidal iron or alcian blue, consistently demonstrate the surface carbohydrate by binding to sialic acid residues.[22] A glycocalyx can be seen on the kidney brush border but it is much less pronounced than that of the enterocyte. Negative stains, such as phospho-tungstate or uranyl acetate, penetrate the glycocalyx and can reveal other

---

Fig. 5. Ultrastructure of the microvillar core. In transverse section the microfilaments (F-actin) can be seen in symmetrical arrangements, (a) rat kidney, 6 + 1 filaments (from reference 87); (b) human intestine, about 30 filaments (from reference 135); (c) chicken intestine, treatment with Mg^{2+} reveals the cross-bridges (α-actinin) linking the actin filaments to the membrane (from reference 20); (d) microvillus, as (c), after treatment with Triton X-100; the membrane has been removed leaving the core structures (from reference 20); (e) electron-dense material (DT) seen at the tips of microvilli (chicken intestine from reference 20); (f) terminal web, a zone of densely interlacing filaments below the brush border (rat intestine). Bar = 100 nm.

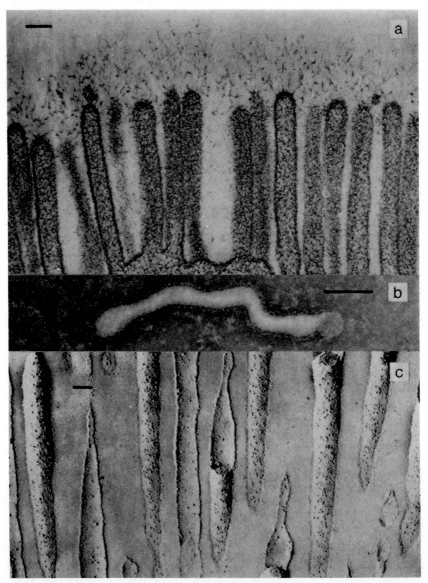

Fig. 6. Ultrastructural details of the microvillar membrane. (a) Glycocalyx—the polysaccharide "fuzz" on the surface of bat intestinal microvilli (from reference 22). (b) Negative staining by uranyl acetate to reveal surface knobs on a rabbit kidney microvillus. (c) Freeze-etched preparation of chicken intestinal brush border showing intramembranous particles (from reference 25). Bar = 100 nm.

surface features. Knobs, 6–10 nm diameter, protrude from the luminal surface of intestinal and kidney microvilli[23, 24, 87] (Fig. 6b). Freeze-etch studies[25] show numerous intramembranous particles, about 9 nm diameter, randomly distributed (Fig. 6c).

IV. Chemical Composition of Microvilli

Brush border preparations contain about 60% protein, 30% lipid and 10% carbohydrate expressed in relation to the dry mass. These values are unremarkable, being similar to those for, say, liver plasma membranes. If the core proteins are removed before analysis the proportion of protein falls to about 50%, a value similar to that reported for the erythrocyte membrane. The detailed analyses that have been made on intestine[9, 26] and kidney[27–29] brush border or microvillus preparations show too much variation to make average values worth calculating from data derived from different species, tissues and preparations. However it is clear that like other plasma membranes, the microvillar membrane is rich in cholesterol. It also contains a high proportion of glycolipids: the molar ratio of cholesterol to phospholipid to glycolipid being about $1:1:2$.[26] Thus glycolipids presumably contribute some of the carbohydrate of the glycocalyx. The sugars identified in microvillus preparations include hexoses, hexosamines and sialic acid, the last accounting for as much as 15–20% of the total carbohydrate in kidney microvilli.

V. Enzymes of the Microvillar Membrane

Most of our information concerning the enzymology of microvilli has come from the study of purified fractions of brush borders or of microvilli obtained from either kidney or intestine. The reliability of such information depends crucially on the quality of the subcellular preparation and this in turn depends on adequate monitoring of the fractionation by microscopy and by the assay of enzymes that are characteristic of this membrane. Electron microscopy using histochemical methods on intact tissue has also been informative. An amino-peptidase, for example, has been demonstrated by incubating slices of kidney cortex with a 'chromogenic' substrate, L-leucine 4-methoxy-2-naphthyl-amide.[30] The aromatic amine released by the enzyme can be detected by a diazo reaction that leads to the deposition of an insoluble, electron-dense product. The localization of phosphatases, e.g. alkaline phosphatase, may be demonstrated by the deposition of another electron-dense product, lead phosphate, if the tissue is incubated with a suitable substrate in the presence of lead citrate.[31] Application of these methods to kidney and intestinal mucosa has shown a high concentration of the aminopeptidase and alkaline phosphatase in the brush border of the kidney proximal tubule cell and the enterocyte. While this type of enzyme localization has been successfully applied to a few enzymes, the more conventional approach is to assay enzymes in purified membrane fractions. Provided that an enzyme is uniquely located on microvilli, the purified fraction should show a handsome enrichment in specific activity compared with the original cell homogenate. Experience in several different laboratories using different procedures to purify microvilli or brush borders has indicated that marker enzymes should be enriched 15- to 20-fold when prepared from kidney cortex or from gut mucosal scrapings. The proof that other enzymes are also located in microvilli depends on the demonstration of comparable enrichment values. There are, however, two qualifications to this principle. The same enzyme (or a similar activity) may be located elsewhere in the cell, in which case the enrichment will be less than that of an enzyme uniquely located in microvilli. Another possibility is that an endogenous inhibitor or activator may be lost during the preparation of the microvilli so that the microvillus preparation has either an exaggerated or depressed enrichment value. The enzymes that have been assigned to microvilli from kidney or intestine are shown in Tables 1, 2 and 3. All are hydrolases capable of splitting peptide, glycoside or ester bonds. While there are obvious similarities between the two types of microvilli, they should not be regarded as

TABLE 1

Microvillar peptidases

Name	EC No.	Subunit mol. wt. $(\times 10^{-3})$	Active site	Tissue*	References
Neutral endopeptidase	3.4.24.–	95	Zn^{2+}	K, I	32, 33, 34
Aminopeptidase M	3.4.11.2	160	Zn^{2+}	K, I	35, 36, 37
Aminopeptidase A	3.4.11.7	—	$?Me^{2+}$	K, I	38, 39, 40
Dipeptidyl peptidase IV	3.4.14.– or 3.4.21.–	130	Serine	K, I	41, 42, 43
Peptidyl dipeptidase (angiotensin I converting enzyme)	3.4.15.1		Zn^{2+}	K	44, 45
Aminopeptidase P (X-prolyl aminopeptidase)	3.4.11.9			K	46, 47
Carboxypeptidase P (prolyl carboxypeptidase)	3.4.12.–			K	47, 48
γ-Glutamyl transferase	2.3.2.2	27. 54		K, I	49, 50, 101
Enterokinase	3.4.21.9		Serine	D	51, 52

* K, kidney; I, intestine; D, duodenum.

TABLE 2

Intestinal brush border glycosidases

Name	EC No.	Subunit mol. wt. ($\times 10^{-3}$)	Inhibitors	Effect of papain	References
Glucoamylase (γ-amylase)	3.2.1.3	(36% carbohydrate)	Tris, phlorizin	Released	57, 58
Trehalase	3.2.1.28	90	Tris, phlorizin	Not released (released by trypsin)	59, 60
Sucrase	3.2.1.48	120	Tris	Released	61, 62
Isomaltase	3.2.1.10	140	Tris	Released	
Lactase	3.2.1.23		Tris, phlorizin	Released	
Glycosylceramidase (phlorizin hydrolase)	3.2.1.45, 46, 62	(17% carbohydrate)	(not inhibited by Tris)	Released	58, 63, 64, 65, 66

TABLE 3

Microvillar phosphatases

Name	EC No.	Tissue*	Notes	References
Alkaline phosphatase	3.1.3.1	K, I, P	Broadly specific monoesterase; EDTA, phenylalanine inhibitory	54, 75, 8
5′-Nucleotidase	3.1.3.5	K	Hydrolyses AMP. In I it is a basolateral marker and hydrolysis of AMP in K may be due to alkaline phosphatase	6
Phosphodiesterase I	3.1.4.1	K	Hydrolyses oligonucleotides	76
D-inositol 1 : 2 cyclic phosphate 2-phosphohydrolase	3.1.4.36	K	Product is D-inositol 1-phosphate	77, 78

* K, kidney; I, intestine; P, placenta.

identical structures; there are clear differences, both qualitative and quantitative, in their complement of enzymes.

A. PEPTIDASES

The group of peptidases (Table 1) identified on kidney microvilli constitutes a very potent set of enzymes capable of degrading a polypeptide to a mixture of amino acids and small peptides. The range of specificities of these peptidases is illustrated in Fig. 7. The attack is mounted by the action of one endopeptidase of broad specificity (it cleaves bonds involving the amino function of hydrophobic amino acids) complemented by an assortment of exopeptidases, two being undiscriminating and three highly specific. If there remain some resistant proline peptides it is possible that they enter the cell and are hydrolysed by specific dipeptidases present in the cytosol.[53] Some, but not all, of the same enzymes have been identified in intestinal brush borders and here their function in the final stages of protein digestion is obvious. Their role in the kidney proximal tubule is far less clear, especially when the very high activities of the microvillar peptidases are compared to the probable load of substrates present in the glomerular filtrate. Even if the least active of the enzymes, the endopeptidase, is taken to be the rate-limiting step in degrading polypeptides, the hydrolytic potential in a rabbit proximal tubule is greater than 20 mg of glucagon (or other peptide of that size) per minute.[54] The endopeptidase is unable to degrade intact insulin and larger proteins[32] so that its attack is

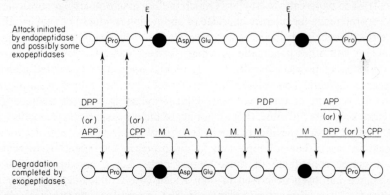

Fig. 7. The specificities of kidney microvillar peptidases. The possible mode of attack is illustrated by a model peptide of 13 amino acid residues. The attack is initiated by the neutral endopeptidase (E) cleaving adjacent to hydrophobic amino acid residues (shown ●) yielding three peptides. Some limited attack by exopeptidases may also occur at this stage, but their role is likely to predominate in the second stage which brings about the degradation of the three peptides to free amino acids and, perhaps, some X-Pro dipeptides. Enzymes: A, aminopeptidase A; APP, aminopeptidase P; CPP, carboxypeptidase P; DPP, dipeptidyl peptidase IV; E, neutral endopeptidase; M, aminopeptidase M; PDP, peptidyl dipeptidase (angiotensin I converting enzyme).

probably limited to simple single chain peptides, no larger than, say, 50 amino acid residues, and the load of such susceptible substrates in the glomerular filtrate is several orders of magnitude less than the ability of the brush border to hydrolyse them. The need for this excessively efficient battery of peptidases is unclear, especially since another means of uptake of polypeptides and proteins, involving pinocytosis, functions in the same cells.

B. GLYCOSIDASES

If the kidney brush border has so far proved to be the more fruitful field of study for membrane-bound peptidases, the intestinal brush border occupies a similar place in regard to glycosidases. Their role in the final stages of carbohydrate digestion is apparent and their importance to health is emphasized by the symptoms that occur as a result of various human genetic deficiencies of disaccharidases in the intestinal mucosa. As a group these enzymes show many similarities in molecular and enzymic properties and often show a somewhat confusing overlap in their specificities (for comprehensive reviews of intestinal glycosidases, see Semenza[55,56]). Maltase, for example, does not appear in the activities listed in Table 2, yet maltose is well hydrolysed by microvillus preparations—probably by at least three enzymes—each with a broader specificity than their usual names imply. In the kidney brush border only trehalose and maltose are known to be hydrolysed.

One enzyme, glucoamylase (γ-amylase, maltase), attacks α-1,4 glycans, but in contrast to pancreatic α-amylase (which prefers macromolecular substrates), it has a preference for oligosaccharides of about nine residues in chain length.[57] Since the glycocalyx behaves as an immobile ion-exchange matrix which binds α-amylase and other pancreatic enzymes (for review see Ugolev & deLaey[67]) the digestion of polysaccharides can be looked upon as a concerted activity between pancreatic and microvillar membrane enzymes taking place in the microenvironment of the membrane. Glucoamylase hydrolyses maltose and therefore accounts for some, though not all, of the mucosal maltase activity.

Trehalase is very specific for the hydrolysis of α,α-trehalose, a disaccharide present in insect haemolymph and in mushrooms. The sugar is, therefore, not a major constituent of most human diets. Yet a hereditary trehalose intolerance has been described in man which causes diarrhoea and may be confused with mushroom intoxication.[68] The enzyme therefore has a role in digestion but its presence in kidney microvilli[69] is not readily explained.

Two activities, isomaltase and sucrase appear to be present as a complex in the membrane. When purified, the complex is a dimeric structure with two non-identical subunits,[61] each possessing one of the two activities and which can be dissociated by treatments such as citraconylation.[62] This pair of enzymes are the most studied and best understood of the intestinal glycosidases. Sucrase is not absolutely specific, since it also hydrolyses other substrates such as maltose and maltotriose. Similarly, isomaltase not only splits the 1,6-α-glycoside link in isomaltose, but similar bonds in other disaccharides and oligosaccharides such as isomaltulose and α-amylase limit dextrins. The two enzymes appear in the intestinal mucosa soon after birth in most animals. In man, however, they are present at high levels before birth and the two activities are equally depressed in the hereditary condition of sucrose–isomaltose malabsorption. Another pair of enzymes which exist in a complex are lactase and glycosylceramidase. The latter enzyme is identical to phlorizin hydrolase, i.e. an enzyme that can split phlorizin into glucose and the aglycone, phloretin. However the most likely natural substrates for this glycosidase are the complex lipids in which a ceramide (N-acyl sphingosine) is linked by a glycosidic bond to a glucose or galactose residue.[64] Such lipids are constituents of the fat globule membrane of milk and are hydrolysed by the phlorizin hydrolase subunit in the rat, though by the lactase moiety in the monkey.[70] Both enzymes may be regarded as β-glycosidases and are therefore not so specific as their names might imply. Their differences may depend on the nature of the aglycone-binding subsite at the active centre of each: lactase having a hydrophilic subsite and glycosylceramidase a hydrophobic subsite. The two subunits are also subject to the same kind of biological control, both achieving a maximum activity at birth and declining after weaning.[65] Furthermore both activities are absent in the human condition of lactose malabsorption.

C. PHOSPHATASES, KINASES AND NUCLEOTIDE CYCLASES

The attribution of many of the enzymes in this group is less well defined than in the two previous groups. In particular the presence of basolateral membranes in a brush border fraction may easily obscure the true enzyme location.

Both enterocytes and kidney proximal tubule cells are strikingly polarized, the brush border at the luminal pole being demarcated from the basolateral membrane by the desmosomal complex. This junction is thought to prevent the lateral diffusion of membrane proteins and thus preserves the distinctive enzyme and protein profiles of the two regions of the plasma membrane. Fractionation methods designed to purify specialized membranes are always imperfect; contamination by other membranes may confuse the interpretation of enzyme studies. A very elegant approach to localizing enzymes in the brush border and basolateral membranes of kidney proximal tubule cells has been developed by Schmidt & Dubach.[71] They developed microdissection techniques and refined the assay methods for ATPases. Their approach overcame the problem of cross-contamination since the source of the membrane was monitored microscopically. They were able to establish that the $(Na^+ + K^+)$-activated ATPase is uniquely located in the basal pole of the cell. The presence of this enzyme in microvillus fractions therefore represents contamination with fragments of basolateral membrane.

Nevertheless, nearly all of our information about enzyme locations has depended on subcellular fractionation methods requiring centrifugation[72, 73] or free-flow electrophoresis.[74] The peptidases and glycosidases described in Sections V.A and V.B are well characterized as enzymes uniquely located in the brush border membrane. Only three, or possibly four, phosphatases can be regarded in the same light; the four enzymes clearly located in the brush border are listed in Table 3. The best-characterized brush border phosphatase is alkaline phosphatase. This dimeric Zn^{2+}-containing glycoprotein enzyme has a subunit molecular weight in the range 66,000 to 80,000. It is a component of the brush border isolated from intestine, kidney and placenta and has been purified from all three sources.[79] Antibodies to the intestinal and placental enzymes cross-react with these, but not with the kidney enzyme.[79] As its name suggests, the enzyme has a broad specificity and an alkaline (pH 10·5) pH optimum. It can be affinity labelled at acid pH with inorganic phosphate (see Section V.A). The physiological role of this enzyme, in common with many other brush border enzymes, is unknown. 5′-Nucleotidase is also sometimes cited as a kidney brush border marker enzyme. This enzyme dephosphorylates 5′-nucleotides at neutral pH. However, the residual activity of alkaline phosphatase at neutral pH values is probably sufficient to account for this enzymic activity.[6] It is interesting to note that, in the intestine, 5′-nucleotidase has been shown to be a marker enzyme for basolateral membranes. Two distinct phosphodiesterases have been shown to be located in the kidney brush border membrane. The first, phosphodiesterase I,[76] acts as an exonuclease, cleaving 5′-nucleotides from oligonucleotides. The second, D-inositol 1:2 cyclic phosphate 2-phosphohydrolase[77, 78] converts D-inositol 1:2 cyclic phosphate to D-inositol 1-phosphate.

There are now an increasing number of reports of other phosphatases and phosphokinases having been identified in brush border membranes. However, sometimes enrichment values are not quoted, or if they are given, the values are low, suggesting non-unique locations. These enzymes in this category are:

Mg^{2+}-activated ATPase (kidney) (EC 3.6.1.3);[6, 69, 74]
HCO_3^--activated ATPase (kidney) (EC 3.6.1.3);[80, 81]
myosin-like (K^+ EDTA)-activated ATPase (intestine) (EC 3.6.1.3);[82]
phosphoprotein phosphatase (kidney) (EC 3.1.3.16);[83]
cyclic-AMP phosphodiesterase (kidney) (EC 3.1.4.17);[84]
cyclic-AMP-dependent and -independent protein kinases (kidney) (EC 2.7.1.37)[83, 85]

Further work may well provide confirmation for the unique location of these enzymes in the microvillar membrane, but for the present it may be better to regard the evidence as tentative rather than proven.

VI. Proteins of the Microvillar Core

In electron micrographs (see Section III.A) the microvillar core consists of an ordered bundle of microfilaments inserted into densely staining material at the microvillar tip. The microfilaments are cross-linked to each other and to the membrane. We can now ask more detailed questions about the nature of these proteins and how they interact with each other and with the membrane.

A. ACTIN

In 1969, Ishikawa et al.[86] introduced a specific staining technique for non-muscle actin in situ. The method involves rendering plasma membrane permeable to macromolecules by treatment with glycerol and then treating the tissue with a tryptic fragment of myosin. This fragment, heavy meromyosin (HMM), binds specifically to actin filaments in a directionally polarized manner and is sufficiently large to be seen on the electron microscope. When this technique was applied to intestinal tissue, the microvillar core filaments were "decorated" with HMM (Fig. 8). Detailed examination of the microfilaments in intestinal[18] and renal[87] brush borders showed that the microfilaments were composed of globular subunits arranged into double helical strands very similar in appearance to muscle F-actin.

All brush border and microvillus preparations so far examined contain a protein of subunit molecular weight 42,000. It is present in large amounts, comprising about 10% of the microvillar protein. When such preparations are solubilized by heating with SDS and thiols, this protein migrates during electrophoresis in polyacrylamide gels with a mobility identical to that of muscle actin. The protein has now been purified from intestinal brush borders[88] and kidney microvilli[89] and is clearly an actin. It is similar to other actins with regard to its subunit molecular weight, amino acid composition, polymerization properties and activation of myosin ATPase activity. The biochemical characterization of microvillar actin is supported by microscopical evidence such as the binding by brush borders of antibodies raised to smooth muscle actin[90] as well as the decoration of the filaments by HMM.[86,89]

B. ACTIN-ASSOCIATED PROTEINS

The presence of actin within the microvilli suggests that analogies might be drawn between the sarcomere and the brush border. Other muscle proteins

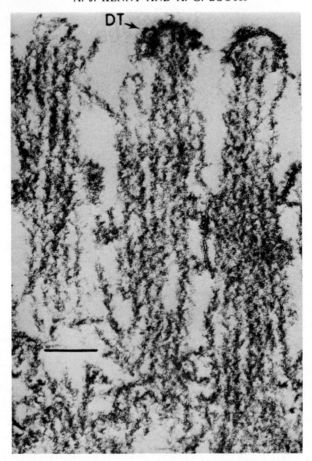

Fig. 8. The appearance of the core microfilaments in microvilli (chicken intestine) after treatment with heavy meromyosin (HMM). The HMM arrowheads are bound to and indicate the polarity of the F-actin filaments. DT, densely staining material at tips (see also Fig. 5e) (from reference 20). Bar = 100 nm.

might be expected to be present within the microvillar core. An obvious possibility is myosin, but it is now clear that although a myosin-like protein is probably present in the terminal web region of the brush border,[20] it is not present within the microvilli.[89] A tropomyosin-like protein has been partially purified from intestinal brush borders,[82] which, like other non-muscle tropomyosins, has a lower molecular weight than the muscle protein. This protein has been obtained from brush border preparations and it is impossible to know whether it is restricted to the microvilli, to the terminal web or is present in both regions of the brush border. There is no report to date of the presence of a troponin complex being identified in brush borders.

Specific antibody staining techniques[91] have shown α-actinin to be a component of the brush border. This protein was originally identified in skeletal muscle where it cross-links actin filaments at the Z-band.[92] It has a subunit molecular weight of 95,000–100,000 and is a rod-shaped molecule 30 nm long and 2 nm in diameter.[93] These dimensions are similar to those of the cross-bridges observed in the microvillar core. An α-actinin-like protein can be co-extracted with actin from brush borders and microvilli[82, 89] and is present in sufficient quantities to account for the observed cross-bridging material. Furthermore, the F-actin in such extracts appears in bundles—typical of the effect *in vitro* of α-actinin on actin.[19]

It is now accepted that the material cross-linking the actin filaments and bracing them to the membrane along the length of the microvillus is α-actinin. However, the nature of the densely staining material at the microvillar tip is a matter of some conjecture. This region of the microvillus is stained by fluorescent anti-α-actinin antibodies and so presumably contains α-actinin bracing the actin filaments to the membrane in a similar manner to the rest of the microvillus. However, its distinct appearance on the electron microscope and its implied properties (discussed in Section VI.C) would argue that there is something special about this region of the microvillus. Along the length of the microvillus the actin filaments are linked to the membrane in a "side-on" manner, but at the tip the filaments connect to the membrane in an "end-on" manner. It would seem reasonable to postulate that perhaps α-actinin mediates the "side-on" interaction and that another protein, visualized as electron-dense staining at the tip, is responsible for the "end-on" interaction. Recently some other, high subunit molecular weight, actin-associated proteins have been described, e.g. macrophage actin-binding protein[94] and the smooth muscle protein, filamin.[95] They also have the property of associating with the plasma membrane. In the case of the macrophage, electron micrographs of the pseudo-podia (Fig. 9a) show material at the tips that closely resembles that seen at the microvillar tip; its identity has yet to be established but its distribution is consistent with the properties of actin-binding protein.

C. POLYMERIZATION OF MICROVILLAR ACTIN—ITS IMPLICATIONS

The core microfilaments can be labelled with HMM to give a characteristic "arrowhead structure" (see Section VI.A). All actins can be labelled in this way and this technique has been useful in studies of how actin polymerizes. The HMM "arrowheads" point in the direction in which an actin filament would move relative to a myosin molecule during contraction. The HMM arrowheads thus reveal the polarity of the actin. When monomers of muscle actin add on to a length of F-actin labelled with HMM, they can be seen to add on almost

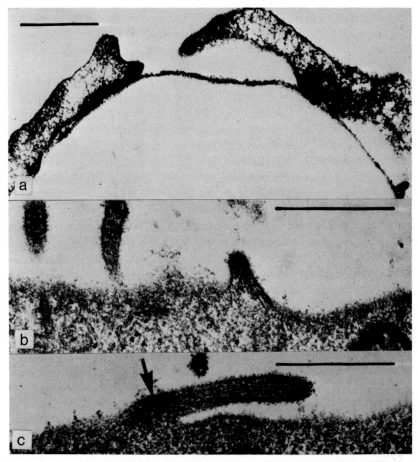

Fig. 9. The generation of microvilli. (a) Rabbit macrophage showing the presence of electron-dense material at the tips of pseudopodia engulfing an oil droplet (from reference 94). (b) and (c) Two stages in the regeneration of microvilli after isolated pieces of salamander intestine had been exposed to high hydrostatic pressures (see Section VI.C). The reappearance of the microvilli seems to be "seeded" by the patch of electron-dense material associated with the membrane; arrow in (c) indicates the possible generation point for a second microvillus (from reference 96). Bar = 0·5 μm.

exclusively to the end from which the arrowheads point. In the case of microvillar actin, the arrowheads point away from the tip. This means that, during the formation of a microvillus, actin monomers must be added to the lengthening microfilaments at the tip.

If isolated pieces of intestine are exposed to high hydrostatic pressures, 6500 p.s.i. (44,850 kPa) the microvilli disappear and the apical membrane becomes relatively smooth. The reformation of microvilli after their pressure-induced disappearance, has been studied by Tilney & Cardell.[96] The first stage in the formation of a microvillus is the attachment of the densely staining material to the cytoplasmic face of the plasma membrane (Fig. 9b). This material then appears to nucleate the formation of the microfilament bundle and the microvillus "grows" out from the flat plasma membrane (Fig. 9c). If the microfilaments grow by actin polymerization at the tip at the site of the densely staining material, the tip protein may well be involved in the polymerization process.

It follows that during its growth, the microfilament bundle and the α-actinin cross-bridges must move relative to the membrane. Little is known about the α-actinin–membrane interaction, in particular we do not know whether the α-actinin molecules interact with specific membrane proteins or with the polar lipid head-groups. Tilney & Mooseker[25] examined the intestinal brush border with freeze-etching techniques. They were unable to observe any correlation between the pattern of intramembranous particles and actin–membrane cross-bridges. However, this does not preclude the possibility of such an interaction occurring. It is known that the transmembrane portion of some microvillar proteins is very small relative to the rest of the molecule (see Section VII.B). If the α-actinin interacted with such a protein, the transmembrane portion would probably be too small to be visualized by freeze-etching studies.

VII. Topology of the Microvillar Proteins

The isolation of microvillar proteins requires an initial solubilizing step. Proteins that are not intrinsic to the membrane, i.e. not anchored by a hydrophobic domain to the lipid bilayer, may be solubilized by treatment with simple salt solutions or with EDTA. Such proteins are extrinsic, attached to the membrane by ionic bonds. Core proteins may be eluted by treatment with 5 mM 2-mercaptoethanol and 0.5 M NaCl; the extract contains actin, α-actinin and another unidentified protein of 180,000 subunit molecular weight.[89] However, no enzymes can be solubilized by such treatments—they require the use of either a proteinase or a detergent. In disorganizing membrane structure, non-ionic detergents release proteins in a state resembling their form in the membrane. Proteinases such as papain or trypsin can release those proteins that are situated with their bulk superficial to the membrane and with a susceptible peptide bond exposed to attack. Proteinase-released proteins therefore lack that part of the polypeptide chain that was associated with the lipid bilayer and possibly with the internal surface of the membrane. In this section we are concerned with some of the molecular properties of the microvillar proteins, in particular the identity of the subunits resolved by electrophoresis and with the nature of the intramembranous domain that serves as an anchor and may extend to the inner surface

A. IDENTIFICATION OF BRUSH BORDER ENZYMES BY GEL ELECTROPHORESIS

Membrane proteins can be solubilized by sodium dodecyl sulphate (SDS) and resolved according to subunit molecular weight by electrophoresis in polyacrylamide gels. There are many different gel systems in use and so it is sometimes difficult to make comparisons of patterns obtained by different workers. In Fig. 10 we have redrawn gel scans for microvillar membranes obtained from kidney,[89] intestine[131] and syncytiotrophoblast,[8] so that all three are on the same scale of subunit molecular weights. A prominent protein of apparent molecular weight 42,000 is a feature of all three membranes and is attributed to actin in the microvillar core. Periodic acid-Schiff-stained gels show that several microvillar proteins are glycoproteins. Apart from two bands of very high molecular weights, most of the major proteins in the range 90,000 to 180,000 molecular weight are glycoproteins and contribute to the glyco-calyx.

There are two main approaches to identifying the stained bands seen on SDS-polyacrylamide gel electrophoresis of microvilli. First the membrane can be dissolved in SDS in mild conditions so that enzymic activities survive and can be directly detected in the gel. For this purpose the membrane samples are neither heated nor reduced with thiols. This technique has been used to locate human[97] and hamster[98] intestinal enzymes on gels. Similarly, pig kidney alkaline phosphatase and phosphodiesterase I activities have been found on gels, with mobilities corresponding to apparent molecular weights of 160,000 and 120,000 respectively.[89] However, this approach has certain disadvantages. Since the enzymes retain activity, they are not fully denatured and may retain oligomeric structure, so that estimates of their subunit molecular weights taken from the gels may not be reliable. Furthermore, usually only a fraction of the original activity of the sample survives solubilization, so that most of the enzyme protein runs as inactive denatured protein, probably with a different mobility. Hence the identification of an enzyme with stained bands is unreliable because the activity may be due to a small amount of native enzyme protein co-electrophoresing with a larger amount of a different denatured protein.

For these reasons, we and other workers have chosen to adopt an alternative approach. This involves identifying the enzymes after complete denaturation and reduction of the membrane proteins. There are several methods of achieving this. First, individual enzymes can be affinity labelled with a covalent radioactive label before solubilization. Provided that the enzyme is uniquely labelled, its position on the gel is revealed by the radioactivity. In this way, pig kidney dipeptidyl peptidase IV has been affinity labelled with [^{32}P]di-isopropyl phosphorofluoridate[89] and human placenta[8] and pig kidney[89] alkaline

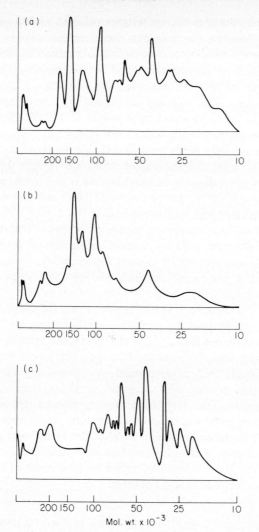

Fig. 10. Microvillar proteins, stained for protein after SDS-polyacrylamide gel electrophoresis. Densitometric scans of (a) kidney, (b) intestine and (c) syncytiotrophoblast microvillar proteins. Redrawn from references 89, 131, 8.

phosphatases by [^{32}P]inorganic phosphate. Secondly, the manner in which the membrane proteins fragment when treated with proteinases such as papain or trypsin can be used to identify enzymes. For example, aminopeptidase M can be solubilized from the pig kidney microvillar membrane by treating the membrane with either trypsin or papain. When purified and examined by electrophoresis in SDS, the aminopeptidase M is found to be composed of three glycoprotein subunits of molecular weights 140,000, 95,000 and 50,000. When the microvillar membrane is examined after electrophoresis in SDS, there is no band visible with a mobility corresponding to a molecular weight of 140,000. However, there is a glycoprotein band whose mobility corresponds to a molecular weight of 160,000 and, when the membrane is treated with papain before analysis, this band is greatly diminished and a new band appears with a mobility corresponding to a molecular weight of 140,000. When the material solubilized from the membrane is examined on SDS gels, bands with mobilities identical to the subunits of the purified aminopeptidase M are present. Thus it is clear that at least the subunit of molecular weight 140,000 found in preparations of pig kidney aminopeptidase M is derived from the membrane glycoprotein of subunit molecular weight 160,000 and that on SDS gels, this band can be identified with aminopeptidase M.[89]

A third method involves comparing the properties of membrane proteins as observed in SDS gels with the known properties of given enzymes. For example, the kidney microvillar neutral endopeptidase (Section V.A) purified after treatment of the membrane with toluene and trypsin is a monomeric glycoprotein of molecular weight 93,000 which is not released from the membrane by treatment with salt or papain. From the specific activities of the microvillar membrane and the purified enzyme it is possible to calculate that this enzyme contributes about 4% of the membrane protein. From these data one may predict that the band on SDS gels corresponding to this enzyme should be a major PAS-positive band with a mobility corresponding to a molecular weight greater than or equal to 93,000 and visible on gels of membrane preparations that have had prolonged exposure to papain. Fortunately, only one band meets these criteria. It is a band whose mobility corresponds to a molecular weight of 95,000.[89] (This band also contains the microvillar α-actinin, a carbohydrate-free salt-extractable protein.) Figure 11 shows a diagram of the kidney microvillar proteins resolved by electrophoresis in SDS and the identities of some of them.

B. THE HYDROPHOBIC ANCHOR OF MICROVILLAR ENZYMES

All the hydrolases that have been purified and studied in detail have certain features in common: they are large glycoproteins ($\geqslant$95,000 mol. wt.) with the catalytic site facing externally into the lumen of the gut or kidney tubule. Most, but not all, of these enzymes can be released by treatment of the membrane with a proteinase, papain and trypsin being those most commonly used. The enzymically active proteins that are released are still large hydrophilic proteins, representing that part of the molecule situated external to the lipid bilayer in the intact membrane. Many are dimeric in their solubilized state and it is probable, though not proven in all cases, that they have the same oligomeric form in the

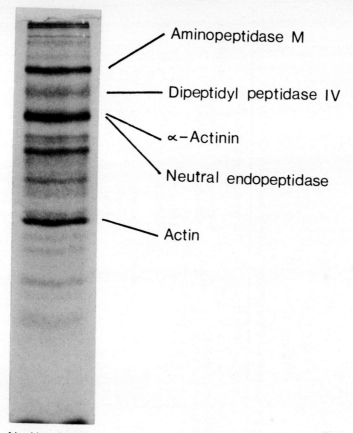

Aminopeptidase M

Dipeptidyl peptidase IV

∝-Actinin

Neutral endopeptidase

Actin

Fig. 11. Identities of some of the protein bands stained after SDS-polyacrylamide gel electrophoresis of kidney microvilli.

membrane. However these proteinase-released enzymes, while retaining all the original hydrolase activity, nevertheless lack the portion of the polypeptide chain that served to anchor the protein in the membrane. The hydrophobic domain of these proteins is of interest for two reasons. First, knowledge of its position in the amino acid sequence of the protein may give a clue regarding the mechanism of assembly by which these enzymes come to be externally facing. Secondly, information on the size and topology of the intramembranous part of a protein may provide an understanding of its role in the organization and function of microvilli. If the hydrophobic domain spans the membrane it may interact with core proteins and may even play a role in transport of solutes across the membrane.

Non-ionic detergents, such as Triton X-100, Lubol-WX and Emulphogen BC720, have been successfully used to solubilize membrane proteins without

TABLE 4

Molecular properties of detergent and proteinase-released forms of some microvillar enzymes

| Enzymes | Source | Mol. wt. ($\times 10^{-3}$) | | Detergent and proteinase forms | | References |
		Membrane (detergent form) subunit mol. wt.	anchor	N-terminal residue(s)	C-terminal residue(s)	
Aminopeptidase M	Intestine	130, 97, 49	9	Different	—	37, 105
Aminopeptidase M	Kidney	160	10	Different	—	36, 89, 100
γ-Glutamyl transferase	Kidney	27 + 54	3	—	Same	101
Dipeptidyl peptidase IV	Kidney	130	4–5	Different	Same	102
Isomaltase	Intestine	140	17	Different	Same	103
Sucrase	Intestine	120	0	Same	Same	103
Alkaline phosphatase	Intestine	64	4	Same	—	104
"Maltases"	Intestine	—	8–10	Different	—	105

—, information not available.

loss of enzyme activity.[99] Microvillar enzymes purified after release by detergents retain the hydrophobic domain. Hence a comparison of the molecular properties of the "detergent form" with the "proteinase form" of an enzyme provides information on the hydrophobic anchor. In SDS-poly-acrylamide gel electrophoresis any non-ionic detergent bound to the protein is displaced by the SDS. A sufficient number of microvillar enzymes have now been investigated (Table 4) for us to attempt some generalizations. The molecular weights of the detergent forms are greater than those of the proteinase forms; the difference in molecular weights being indicative of the size of the anchor. Generally it is relatively small, 3000 to 10,000 mol. wt. or 30 to 100 amino acid residues. Sucrase is an exception: the two forms have identical subunit molecular weights. This is because the sucrase–isomaltase complex is anchored only by the isomaltase subunit, ionic and other inter-actions suffice to bind the two enzymes together. We know nothing of the conformation of the hydrophobic domain within the membrane but we may estimate that a chain of 25–50 amino acids might suffice to traverse the membrane. The molecular size, i.e. the Stokes' radius, of the detergent forms, determined by gel filtration, is usually very much greater than that of the proteinase forms. This is because the hydrophobic domain binds detergent, which, if it comprises a detergent micelle, may represent about 90,000 atomic mass units.[99] The Stokes' radii of the two forms of γ-glutamyl transferase differ by a factor of two.[101] Another demonstration of the presence of bound detergent is seen in "charge shift" electrophoresis. The mobility of the protein with bound non-ionic detergent can be changed when electrophoresed in the presence of an anionic detergent (e.g. deoxycholate) or a cationic detergent (e.g. cetyltrimethylammonium bromide, CTAB).[106]

The part of the amino acid sequence containing the hydrophobic anchor has been determined for intestinal isomaltase.[103] The N-terminal sequence of the 140,000 mol. wt. polypeptide chain is shown in Fig. 12. Residues 10–32 are all hydrophobic, conferring on this domain the requisite properties of an anchor. The papain form lacks this sequence: it is about 150 residues shorter, has a different N-terminal residue but the same pattern of C-terminal residues as the

1   5   10
Ala-Val-Asn-Ala-Phe-Ser-Gly-Leu-Glu-Ile-X-Leu-

15   20
Ile-Val-Leu-Phe-Val-Ile-Val-Phe-Ile-Ile-Ala-Ile-

25   30   35
Ala-Leu-Ile-Ala-Val-Leu-Ala-X-X-X-Pro-Ala-Val

Fig. 12. The amino acid sequence of the N-terminal portion of pig intestinal isomaltase (reference 103).

detergent form. So far, sequences have not been published for other enzymes but the finding for several of them that the two forms differ in the N-terminal residue is consistent with the hydrophobic region being located at or near the N-terminal region of the polypeptide chain. The report[104] that the two forms of intestinal alkaline phosphatase share the same first and second residues at the N-terminus is at variance with this general finding, but consistent with the finding that the two forms behave as similar sized proteins on gel filtration.

The compelling evidence that some, at least, of the microvillar enzymes are anchored by a peptide near the N-terminus shows us that different modes of membrane attachment exist for plasma membrane proteins. In other cells, the attachment of some proteins is at, or adjacent to, the C-terminal sequence, e.g. glycophorin, and the histocompatibility antigens, H2 and HLA (for review, see reference 107). Hence any model for the biosynthesis of plasma membrane proteins must permit either mode of insertion. We know that plasma membrane proteins are synthesized by polyribosomes attached to the endoplasmic reticulum[108]—in this respect similar to secreted proteins. One tempting possibility for proteins like isomaltase might be that shown in Fig. 13.

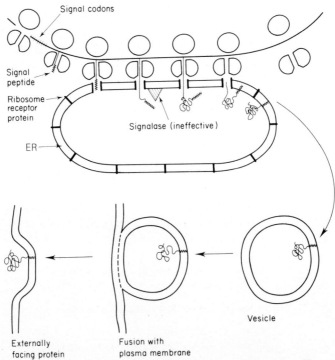

Fig. 13. A hypothetical scheme for the biosynthesis and assembly of a microvillar membrane protein; ER, endoplasmic reticulum (modified after reference 109).

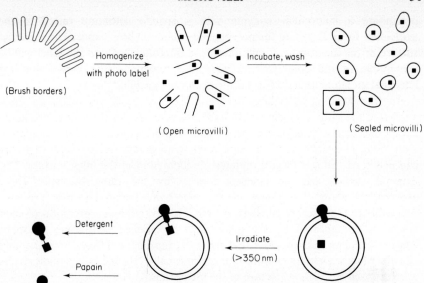

Fig. 14. Scheme by which microvillar proteins may be asymmetrically labelled using a photo-label (nitrophenylazide) covalently linked to a marker protein (modified from reference 110).

Here the hydrophobic signal peptide (for review see Campbell & Blobel[109]) at the N-terminal sequence of the newly synthesized chain is not clipped from the protein by signalase (signal peptidase) but persists and reinserts into the interior surface of the membrane—a surface that could, after fusion with the plasma membrane become the external surface of the cell. However the sequence of isomaltase for the first nine residues is not typical of a signal peptide (which is usually a sequence of about 20 hydrophobic residues); the "anchor" sequence starts only at residue ten. The simple hypothesis that equates the signal and the anchor peptides is therefore not supported by this example.

The extent of the penetration of the hydrophobic anchor can only be ascertained by experiments in which proteins are differentially labelled on the two surfaces of the microvillar membrane, Fig. 14. A very elegant immunological approach to this problem has been made by Louvard et al.[110] The method depends on the finding that when free microvilli are prepared by homogenizing brush borders, their interiors are freely accessible to macro-molecules in the medium. When they are incubated, the microvilli swell and become sealed right-side-out vesicles. It is thus possible to seal in a protein bearing a photoactivated reagent (e.g. human Fab fragment covalently linked to nitrophenylazide). When illuminated, the azide group reacts indiscriminately with any accessible group on the inner surface of the membrane. If the membrane is now dissolved by a non-ionic detergent, it is possible to immunoprecipitate a microvillar enzyme with a specific antibody raised to the proteinase form. If part of the polypeptide chain had been exposed on the inner surface of the membrane, it will have been photolabelled and the label will be identifiable in the immunoprecipitate. This technique has shown that pig intestinal aminopeptidase M is a transmembrane protein.[110]

Another labelling procedure, lactoperoxidase-catalysed iodination, has been applied to the same problem.[111] Here the macromolecules that are sealed in the closed microvillus vesicles are the enzymes required to catalyse the iodination with $^{125}I^-$. The addition of the substrates, glucose and iodide, both of which can penetrate the membrane, initiates the iodination of the inner surface. The external surface can be labelled directly by the same reagents. These experiments show that many of the externally facing enzymes are also accessible to the internal labelling system. However the interpretation of such results is complicated by the occurrence of labelled membrane phospholipids—a finding that suggests that free $^{125}I_2$ may have diffused into the lipid bilayer. Thus we cannot be sure that the internally labelled polypeptide chains were exposed at the inner surface of the membrane.

The intramembranous domains of microvillar proteins can be demonstrated with a photolabelling reagent that is sufficiently hydrophobic to partition into the membrane lipid. When [^{125}I]iodonaphthylazide, introduced in this way, is illuminated, it reacts with the hydrophobic components of the membrane.[112] In rat intestinal microvilli, several polypeptides were so labelled, one of which, referred to as sucrase by the authors,[112] is presumably the isomaltase component. However it is important to realize that this reagent cannot discriminate between proteins that traverse and do not traverse the membrane; it merely provides evidence for a hydrophobic anchor.

VIII. Functional Aspects

The intestinal and renal brush borders have essential roles in transporting a great variety of solutes from the lumen into the cell. Small organic molecules such as sugars and amino acids are taken up by carrier-mediated, Na^+-dependent systems. Macromolecules, in particular proteins, may enter these cells by pinocytosis. The scope of this Essay precludes any attempt to review the very extensive literature dealing with these functions (for reviews see references 113, 114). Nevertheless the account we have given of the enzymes and other proteins of microvilli would be incomplete if we did not make some attempt to relate these molecules to the physiological functions of the brush border. Two questions will be discussed: why are microvillar membranes so rich in hydrolases which, in the case of the kidney, seem disproportionate to physiological needs and what purpose is served by the contractile proteins of the microvillus core and terminal web?

A. ALTERNATIVE ROLES FOR MICROVILLAR HYDROLASES

In the intestine the need for a range of hydrolytic enzymes to cope with a wide variety of substrates derived from the partial digestion of dietary components is readily understood. The role of a similar complement of enzymes in the kidney proximal tubule is far from obvious. It is doubtful if there would be any significant nutritional loss if all the peptide hormones in the glomerular filtrate were excreted unchanged in the urine. Perhaps their inactivation and hydrolysis in the proximal tubule is necessary to eliminate bizarre actions in the distal tubule, but there is no evidence to support this idea. One possibility that has been considered is that these hydrolytic enzymes may play a role in transport.

The γ-glutamyl cycle has been proposed by Meister as a mechanism by which amino acids are transported (for reviews see references 115, 116). The cycle is summarized in Fig. 15. It shows how γ-glutamyl transferase in the microvillar membrane transfers an amino acid into the cell as γ-Glu-amino acid, which is split by another enzyme, γ-glutamyl cyclotransferase to release the free amino acid. The energy input for the cycle is concerned in regenerating glutathione, the donor of the γ-Glu residue; the stoicheiometry is three ATP per amino acid transported. Although the cycle is feasible in the sense that all the enzymes are present in the kidney, there are some major difficulties in accepting that it accounts for amino acid transport *in vivo*. One of the six

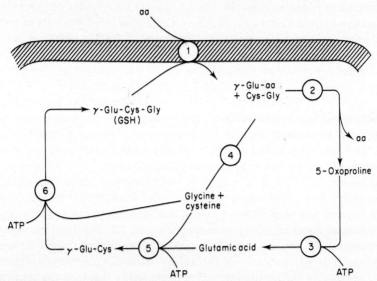

Fig. 15. Meister's γ-glutamyl cycle.[115] Enzymes: 1, γ-glutamyl transferase; 2, γ-glutamyl cyclotransferase; 3, 5-oxoprolinase; 4, cysteinylglycine; 5, γ-glutamylcysteine synthetase; 6, glutathione synthetase.

enzymes, 5-oxoprolinase, has a very low activity relative to the others and its substrate, 5-oxoproline, might be expected to accumulate in cells if the system were overloaded with amino acids.[117] Some amino acids do have this effect but others do not and there is a poor correlation in these effects with the efficiency of different amino acids to be acceptors of the γ-Glu residue in the γ-glutamyl transferase step. Additionally the specificity of γ-glutamyl cyclotransferase is limited, e.g. γ-Glu-Phe is not a substrate and hence phenylalanine could not be transported by this means. Of course, it is possible to argue that even if the cycle as a whole does not function in amino acid transport, the initial step, involving γ-glutamyl transferase, might still be an essential component. Even this limited role seems to be excluded by results from investigations on a patient exhibiting glutathionuria in whom the enzymic defect was shown to be that of γ-glutamyl transferase. The patient did not show an amino aciduria, which would be predicted if the enzyme had a role in transport, not could any defect of amino acid transport be detected in cultured fibroblasts from the patient.[118,119]

If the γ-glutamyl cycle has failed to fulfil its postulated role, can we implicate other hydrolases in transport? One experimental approach has been to create artificial systems in which solubilized membrane proteins are incorporated into artificial phospholipid membranes. An early reconstitution experiment involved the incorporation of the sucrase–isomaltase complex into a "black" membrane. Without the complex, the black lipid membrane was impermeable to sugars. When the sucrase–isomaltase complex was present and radioactive sucrose introduced on one side, the hydrolytic products of sucrose were found on the other side of the membrane.[120] Such a system is not Na^+ dependent and it cannot transport monosaccharides. It did, however, seem to account for a well-known phenomenon, the "kinetic advantage" whereby the hexoses combined in a disaccharide are taken up by the intestine faster than they would be in the free form.[121] The same relationship has been shown for dipeptides and free amino acids.[122] The experiments with sucrase–isomaltase are difficult to evaluate because the preparation used was a papain-released form and therefore lacked the hydrophobic anchor, moreover the sucrase subunit is not an intrinsic protein and can hardly mediate in a transmembrane effect. More useful would be studies in which detergent forms of proteins are reconstituted in artifical membranes. A crude Triton X-100 extract of renal brush borders has been shown to effect Na^+-dependent glucose transport.[123] The detergent form of kidney aminopeptidase M has also been incorporated into liposomes[124] but evidence that such a reconstituted system transports amino acids is still awaited. Of the kidney microvillar peptidases, three are major proteins of the membrane, which might imply that they are involved in an essential function. We know that amino acids are transported by four "group-specific" systems common to both the intestine and kidney.[114] There is some general similarity between the specificities of these transport systems and some of the peptidases, e.g. aminopeptidase A and the system transporting aspartic and glutamic acids; aminopeptidase M and the "neutral" group and there are several peptidases that recognize proline residues, in common with the imino-glycine transport group. Tempting though these speculations are, there is still no evidence to identify the peptidases with the transport systems and the lack of Na^+ dependence for the former is a further obstacle in this regard.

B. THE CONTRACTILE PROTEINS

The microvillar core contains actin filaments extending deeply into the apical cytoplasm of the cell, to the region of the terminal web. The finding of contractile proteins in non-muscle cells is now commonplace and often a correlation with movement of some sort is apparent. In the case of kidney and intestinal brush borders we must now enquire if microvillar actin has a similar function. Microvilli, with a diameter of $0\cdot1$ μm, are just beyond the resolution of light microscopy, so investigation of unfixed preparations by phase-contrast microscopy poses difficulties. In spite of this, some observers have noted concerted movements when brush borders of intact cells from kidney[125] or intestine[126] are examined in this way. Although random Brownian movement could be excluded, it was not possible to be certain that the movement observed had its origin in the microvilli, since contraction at other sites within the cells might have achieved the same effect. Isolated brush borders from the intestine have also been observed to contract, using Nomarski light optics.[127] Here the stimulus was the addition of ATP to a medium containing divalent cations and the effect was a change from an oval to a more rounded shape. The same workers were able to examine the relaxed and contracted forms in the electron microscope. The effect of ATP was achieved by a pinching-in of the lateral plasma membrane in the region of the desmosome complex causing a change in shape of the preparation. In intact tissue, the lateral membranes would resist this inward movement and the result of such a contraction might instead be manifested on the microvilli themselves, as shown in Fig. 16a. Mooseker[82] has used a different preparation—"demembranated" brush borders, produced by treatment with Triton X-100 (cf. Fig. 5d). The core proteins resist the detergent and the dissolution of the membrane seems to remove some constraints from the core filaments so that when stimulated by ATP they retract into and through the filaments of the terminal web causing a dramatic shortening of the microvillar skeletons, as shown diagrammatically in Fig. 16b. The essential difference in the two hypotheses is the involvement or non-involvement of the tonofilaments that arise from the desmosomal complex and mesh with the actin filaments of the terminal web.

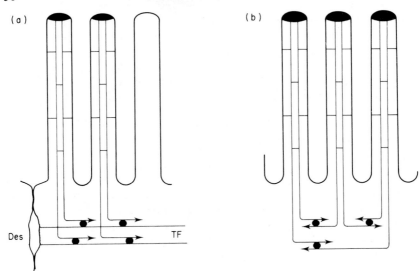

Fig. 16. Two possible means by which microvillar actin can participate in a contractile process. (a) After Rodewald et al.[127], (b) after Mooseker[82]. Des, desmosomal complex; TF, tonofilaments; ●, myosin.

The purposes which this kind of contractility of microvilli might serve are two-fold. First, the efficiency of hydrolysis and uptake of small solutes from the lumen would be increased if there is adequate stirring of the fluid layers in contact with the membrane. Secondly, and perhaps of more general importance for all cell types, is the mechanism by which the membrane in the crypts between adjacent microvilli is first deformed and then pinched off into a pinocytic vesicle. Pinocytosis is a property of most eukaryotic cells and has been shown to be the mechanism by which proteins can be taken up in the kidney,[128] intestine[129] and yolk sac.[130] It is assumed that the process is triggered by the binding of a protein to a surface receptor, but we know nothing of the mechanisms involved in generating a pinocytic vesicle. However, it will be clear from Fig. 16 that a contraction involving the actin filaments of microvilli can partially enclose a fluid droplet which would then require only fusion of the membrane to generate a vesicle.

IX. Concluding Remarks

We have attempted to describe microvilli in molecular terms and to correlate this information with the ultrastructural features of this complex membrane. There are still many unanswered questions. The detailed enzymology of renal and intestinal microvilli is by no means complete and the enzymic differentiation of microvilli in other cells has yet to be studied. But perhaps the outstanding deficiency in our knowledge is our inability to describe the main functions of brush borders—carrier-mediated transport and pinocytosis—in molecular terms. This is currently the subject of intense investigation.

ACKNOWLEDGEMENTS

Electron micrographs not otherwise acknowledged were taken by Douglas Kershaw of this Department. We are very grateful to various authors and journals for permission to reproduce the other electron micrographs.

REFERENCES

1. Rhodin, J. A. G. (1974). *Histology, a Text and Atlas*. Oxford University Press, New York, London and Toronto.
2. Satir, P. (1977). Microvilli and cilia: surface specializations of mammalian cells. In *Mammalian Cell Membranes*, Vol. II. The Diversity of Membranes (Jamieson, G. A. & Robinson, D. M., eds). Butterworths, London, pp. 323–353.
3. Miller, D. & Crane, R. K. (1961). Digestive function of the epithelium of the small intestine. II. Localization of disaccharide hydrolysis in the isolated brush border portion of intestinal epithelial cells. *Biochim. Biophys. Acta* **52**, 293–298.
4. Forstner, G. G., Sabesin, S. M. & Isselbacher, K. J. (1968). Rat intestinal microvillus membranes, purification and biochemical characterization. *Biochem. J.* **106**, 381–390.
5. Thuneberg, L. & Rostgaard, J. (1968). Isolation of brush border fragments from homogenates of rat and rabbit kidney cortex. *Exp. Cell Res.* **51**, 123–140.
6. George, S. G. & Kenny, A. J. (1973). Studies on the enzymology of purified preparations of brush border from rabbit kidney. *Biochem. J.* **134**, 43–57.
7. Wilfong, R. F. & Neville, D. M. (1970). The isolation of a brush border membrane fraction from rat kidney. *J. Biol. Chem.* **245**, 6106–6112.
8. Carlson, R. W., Wada, H. G. & Sussman, H. H. (1976). The plasma membrane of human placenta, isolation of microvillus membrane and characterisation of protein and glycoprotein subunits. *J. Biol. Chem.* **251**, 4139–4146.
9. Louvard, D., Maroux, S., Baratti, J., Desnuelle, P. & Mutaftschiev, S. (1973). On the preparation and some properties of closed membrane vesicles from hog duodenal and jejunal brush border. *Biochim. Biophys. Acta* **291**, 747–763.
10. Schmitz, J., Preiser, H., Maestracci, D., Ghosh, B. K., Cerda, J. J. & Crane, R. K. (1973). Purification of the human intestinal brush border membrane. *Biochim. Biophys. Acta* **323**, 98–112.
11. Booth, A. G. & Kenny, A. J. (1974). A rapid method for the preparation of microvilli from rabbit kidney. *Biochem. J.* **142**, 575–581.
12. Segal, S., McNamara, P. D. & Pepe, L. M. (1977). Transport interaction of cystine and dibasic amino acids in renal brush border vesicles. *Science* **19**, 169–171.
13. Kessler, M., Acuto, O., Storelli, C., Murer, H., Müller, M. & Semenza, G. (1978). A modified procedure for the rapid preparation of efficiently transporting vesicles from small intestinal brush border membranes. Their use in investigating some properties of D-glucose and choline transport systems. *Biochim. Biophys. Acta* **506**, 136–154.

14. Busse, D. & Steinmeyer, G. (1974). Osmotically reactive plasma membrane vesicles prepared from rabbit kidney tubules by mild hypotonic lysis. *Biochim. Biophys. Acta* **345**, 359–372.

15. Schlamowitz, M., Hillman, K., Lichtiger, G. & Ahearn, M. J. (1975). Preparation of IgG-binding membrane vesicles from the microvillar brush border of the fetal rabbit yolk sac. *J. Immunol.* **115**, 296–302.

16. Smith, C. H., Nelson, D. M., King, B. F., Donohue, T. M., Ruzycki, S. M. & Kelley, L. K. (1977). Characterization of a microvillus membrane preparation from human placental membrane syncytiotrophoblast: A morphologic, biochemical and physiologic study. *Amer. J. Obstet. Gynec.* **128**, 190–196.

17. Millington, P. F. & Finean, J. B. (1962). Electron microscope studies of the structure of the microvilli on principal epithelial cells of rat jejunum after treatment in hypo- and hypertonic saline. *J. Cell Biol.* **14**, 125–139.

18. Mukherjee, T. M. & Staehelin, L. A. (1971). The fine-structural organization of the brush border of intestinal epithelial cells. *J. Cell Sci.* **8**, 573–599.

19. Booth, A. G. & Kenny, A. J. (1976). A morphometric and biochemical investigation of the vesiculation of kidney microvilli. *J. Cell Sci.* **21**, 449–463.

20. Mooseker, M. S. & Tilney, L. G. (1975). Organization of an actin filament-membrane complex. Filament polarity and membrane attachment in the microvilli of intestinal epithelial cells. *J. Cell Biol.* **67**, 725–743.

21. Limbrick, A. R. & Finean, J. B. (1970). X-ray diffraction and electron microscope studies of the brush border membrane of guinea-pig intestinal epithelial cells. *J. Cell Sci.* **7**, 373–386.

22. Ito, S. (1965). The enteric surface coat on cat intestinal microvilli. *J. Cell Biol.* **27**, 475–491.

23. Johnson, C. F. (1966). Disaccharidase: localization in hamster intestine brush borders. *Science* **155**, 1670–1672.

24. Nishi, Y., Yoshida, T. O. & Takesue, Y. (1968). Electron microscope studies on the structure of rabbit intestinal sucrase. *J. Mol. Biol.* **37**, 441–444.

25. Tilney, L. G. & Mooseker, M. S. (1976). Actin filament-membrane attachment: are membrane particles involved? *J. Cell Biol.* **71**, 402–416.

26. Forstner, G. G., Tanaka, K. & Isselbacher, K. J. (1968). Lipid composition of the isolated rat intestinal microvillus membrane. *Biochem. J.* **109**, 51–59.

27. Glossmann, H. & Neville, D. M. (1971). Glycoproteins of cell surfaces. A comparative study of three different cell surfaces of the rat. *J. Biol. Chem.* **246**, 6339–6346.

28. Quirk, S. J. & Robinson, G. B. (1972). Isolation and characterization of rabbit kidney brush borders. *Biochem. J.* **128**, 1319–1328.

29. Bode, F., Baumann, K. & Kinne, R. (1976). Analysis of the pinocytic process in rat kidney. Biochemical composition of pinocytic vesicles compared to brush border microvilli, lysosomes and basolateral plasma membranes. *Biochim. Biophys. Acta* **433**, 294–310.

30. Nachlas, M. M., Morris, B., Rosenblatt, D. & Seligman, A. M. (1959). Improvement in the histochemical localization of leucine aminopeptidase with a new substrate, L-leucyl-4-methoxy-2-naphthylamide. *J. Biophys. Biochem. Cytol.* **7**, 261–264.

31. Ernst, S. A. (1975). Transport ATPase cytochemistry: ultrastructural localization of potassium-dependent and potassium-independent phosphatase activities in rat kidney cortex. *J. Cell Biol.* **66**, 586–608.

32. Kerr, M. A. & Kenny, A. J. (1974). The purification and specificity of a neutral endopeptidase from rabbit kidney brush border. *Biochem. J.* **137**, 477–488.

33. Kerr, M. A. & Kenny, A. J. (1974). The molecular weight and properties of a neutral metallo-endopeptidase from rabbit kidney brush border. *Biochem. J.* **137**, 489–495.

34. Kenny, A. J. & Vyas, J. P. Unpublished work.

35. Wacker, H., Lehky, P., Fischer, E. H. & Stein, E. A. (1971). Physical and chemical characterization of pig kidney particulate aminopeptidase. *Helv. Chim. Acta* **54**, 473–485.

36. Wacker, H., Lehky, P., Vanderhaege, F. & Stein, E. A. (1976). On the subunit structure of particulate aminopeptidase from pig kidney. *Biochim. Biophys. Acta* **429**, 546–554.

37. Maroux, S., Louvard, D. & Baratti, J. (1973). The aminopeptidase from hog intestinal brush border. *Biochim. Biophys. Acta* **321**, 282–295.

38. Glenner, G. G. & Folk, J. E. (1961). Glutamyl peptidases in rat and guinea pig kidney slices. *Nature (London)* **192**, 338–340.

39. Glenner, G. G., McMillan, P. J. & Folk, J. E. (1962). A mammalian peptidase specific for the hydrolysis of N-terminal α-L-glutamyl and aspartyl residues. *Nature (London)* **194**, 867.

40. Andria, G., Marzi, A. & Auricchio, S. (1976). α-Glutamyl-β-naphthylamide hydrolase of rabbit small intestine. Localization in the brush border and separation from other brush border peptidases. *Biochim. Biophys. Acta* **419**, 42–50.

41. Hopsu-Havu, V. K., Rintola, P. & Glenner, G. G. (1968). A hog kidney aminopeptidase liberating N-terminal dipeptides. Partial purification and characteristics. *Acta Chem. Scand.* **22**, 299–308.

42. Barth, A., Schulz, H. & Neubert, K. (1974). Untersuchungen zur Reinigung und Charakterisierung der Dipeptidylaminopeptidase IV. *Acta Biol. Med. Germ.* **32**, 157–174.

43. Kenny, A. J., Booth, A. G., George, S. G., Ingram, J., Kershaw, D., Wood, E. J. & Young, A. R. (1976). Dipeptidyl peptidase IV, a kidney brush-border serine peptidase. *Biochem. J.* **155**, 169–182.

44. Ward, P. E., Erdös, E. G., Gedney, C. D., Dowben, R. M. & Reynolds, R. C. (1976). Isolation of membrane-bound renal enzymes that metabolize kinins and angiotensins. *Biochem. J.* **157**, 643–650.

45. Erdös, E. G. (1977). The angiotensin I converting enzyme. *Fedn. Proc. Fedn. Amer. Socs. Exp. Biol.* **36**, 1760–1765.

46. Dehm, P. & Nordwig, A. (1970). The cleavage of prolyl peptides by kidney peptidases. Partial purification of an "X-prolyl-aminopeptidase" from swine kidney microsomes. *Eur. J. Biochem.* **17**, 364–371.

47. Kenny, A. J., Booth, A. G. & Macnair, R. D. C. (1977). Peptidases of the kidney microvillus membrane. *Acta Biol. Med. Germ.* **36**, 1575–1585.

48. Dehm, P. & Nordwig, A. (1970). The cleavage of prolyl peptides by kidney peptidases. Isolation of a microsomal carboxypeptidase from swine kidney. *Eur. J. Biochem.* **17**, 372–377.

49. Tate, S. S. & Meister, A. (1977). Affinity labelling of γ-glutamyl transpeptidase and location of the γ-glutamyl binding site on the light subunit. *Proc. Nat. Acad. Sci. U.S.* **74**, 931–935.

50. Zelazo, P. & Orlowski, M. (1976). γ-Glutamyl transpeptidase of sheep-kidney cortex. Isolation, catalytic properties and dissociation into two polypeptide chains. *Eur. J. Biochem.* **61**, 147–155.

51. Nordstrom, C. & Dahlquist, A. (1970). The cellular localization of enterokinase. *Biochim. Biophys. Acta* **198**, 621–622.

52. Maroux, S., Baratti, J. & Desnuelle, P. (1971). Purification and specificity of porcine enterokinase. *J. Biol. Chem.* **246**, 5031–5039.

53. Josefsson, L., Sjöström, H. & Norén, O. (1977). *Intracellular Hydrolysis of Peptides in Peptide Transport and Hydrolysis.* CIBA Foundation Symposium 50. Elsevier, North Holland, pp. 199–207.

54. Kenny, A. J. & Booth, A. G. (1976). Organization of the kidney proximal-tubule plasma membrane. *Biochem. Soc. Trans.* **4**, 1011–1017.

55. Semenza, G. (1976). Small intestinal disaccharidases: their properties and role as sugar translocators across natural and artificial membranes. In *The Enzymes of Biological Membranes*, Vol. 3 (Martonosi, A., ed.). Plenum Press, New York, pp. 349–382.

56. Semenza, G. (1976). Glycosidases of small intestinal brush borders. In *Membranes and Disease* (Bolis, L., Hoffman, J. F. & Leaf, A., eds). Raven Press, New York, pp. 243–252.

57. Kelly, J. J. & Alpers, D. H. (1973). Properties of human intestinal glyco-amylase. *Biochim. Biophys. Acta* **315**, 113–120.

58. Schlegel-Haueter, S., Hore, P., Kerry, K. R. & Semenza, G. (1972). The preparation of lactase and glucoamylase of rat small intestine. *Biochim. Biophys. Acta* **258**, 506–519.

59. Sasajima, K., Kawachi, T., Sato, S. & Sugimura, T. (1975). Purification and properties of α,α-trehalase from the mucosa of rat small intestine. *Biochim. Biophys. Acta* **403**, 139–146.

60. Nakano, M., Sumi, Y. & Miyakawa, M. (1977). Purification and properties of trehalase from rat intestinal mucosal cells. *J. Biochem. (Tokyo)* **81**, 1041–1049.

61. Cogoli, A., Eberle, A., Sigrist, H., Joss, C., Robinson, E., Mosimann, H. & Semenza, G. (1973). Subunits of the small-intestinal sucrase-isomaltase complex and separation of its enzymatically active isomaltase moiety. *Eur. J. Biochem.* **33**, 40–48.

62. Braun, H., Cogoli, A. & Semenza, G. (1975). Dissociation of small-intestinal sucrase-isomaltase complex into enzymatically active subunits. *Eur. J. Biochem.* **52**, 475–480.

63. Malathi, P. & Crane, R. K. (1969). Phlorizin hydrolase: A β-glucosidase of hamster intestinal brush border membrane. *Biochim. Biophys. Acta* **173**, 245–256.

64. Leese, H. J. & Semenza, G. (1973). On the identity between the small intestinal enzymes phlorizin hydrolase and glycosyl-ceramidase. *J. Biol. Chem.* **248**, 8170–8173.

65. Lorenz-Meyer, H., Blum, A. L., Haemmerli, H. P. & Semenza, G. (1972). A second enzyme defect in aquired lactase deficiency: lack of small-intestinal phlorizin-hydrolase. *Eur. J. Clin. Invest.* **2**, 326–331.

66. Birkenmeier, E. & Alpers, D. H. (1974). Enzymatic properties of rat lactase-phlorizin hydrolase. *Biochim. Biophys. Acta* **350**, 100–112.

67. Ugolev, A. M. & DeLaey, P. (1973). Membrane digestion: a concept of enzymic hydrolysis on cell membranes. *Biochim. Biophys. Acta* **300**, 105–128.

68. Modžaravová-Nohejlova, J. (1973). Trehalase deficiency in a family. *Gastroenterology* **65**, 130–133.

69. Berger, S. J. & Sacktor, B. (1970). Isolation and biochemical characterization of brush border from rabbit kidney. *J. Cell Biol.* **47**, 637–645.

70. Ramaswamy, S. & Radhakrishnan, A. N. (1975). Lactase-phlorizin hydrolase complex from monkey small intestine: purification, properties and evidence for two catalytic sites. *Biochim. Biophys. Acta* **403**, 446–455.

71. Schmidt, U. & Dubach, U. C. (1971). Na K stimulated adenosinetriphosphatase: intracellular localisation within the proximal tubule of the rat nephron. *Pflügers Arch. Ges. Physiol.* **330**, 265–270.

72. Fujita, M., Ohta, H., Kawai, K., Matsui, H. & Nakao, M. (1972). Differential isolation of microvillous and basolateral plasma membranes from intestinal mucosa: mutually exclusive distribution of digestive enzymes and ouabain-sensitive ATPase. *Biochim. Biophys. Acta* **274**, 336–347.

73. Lewis, B. A., Gray, M. G., Coleman, R. & Michell, R. H. (1975). Differences in the enzymic, polypeptide, glycopeptide, glycolipid and phospholipid composition of plasma membranes from the two surfaces of intestinal epithelial cells. *Biochem. Soc. Trans.* **3**, 752–753.

74. Heidrich, H.-G., Kinne, R., Kinne-Saffran, E. & Hannig, K. (1972). The polarity of the proximal tubule cell in rat kidney. Different surface charges for the brush-border microvilli and plasma membranes from the basal infoldings. *J. Cell Biol.* **54**, 232–245.

75. Michell, R. H., Coleman, R. & Lewis, B. A. (1976). Biochemical differentiation of the plasma membrane of the intestinal epithelial cell. *Biochem. Soc. Trans.* **4**, 1017–1020.

76. Glossman, H. & Neville, D. M., Jr. (1972). Phlorizin receptors in isolated kidney brush border membranes. *J. Biol. Chem.* **247**, 7779–7789.

77. Clarke, N. G. & Dawson, R. M. C. (1972). Localization of D-myoinositol 1:2-cyclic phosphate 2-phosphohydrolase in rat kidney. *Biochem. J.* **130**, 229–238.

78. Dawson, R. M. C. & Clarke, N. G. (1973). A comparison of D-inositol 1:2-cyclic phosphate 2-phosphohydrolase with other phosphodiesterases of kidney. *Biochem. J.* **134**, 59–67.

79. Lehmann, F.-G. (1975). Immunological relationship between human placental and intestinal alkaline phosphatase. *Clin. Chim. Acta* **65**, 257–269.

80. Kinne-Saffran, E. & Kinne, R. (1974). Presence of bicarbonate stimulated ATPase in the brush border microvillus membranes of the proximal tubule. *Proc. Soc. Exp. Biol. Med.* **146**, 751–753.

81. Liang, C. T. & Sacktor, B. (1976). Bicarbonate-stimulated ATPase in the renal proximal tubule luminal (brush border) membrane. *Arch. Biochem. Biophys.* **176**, 285–297.

82. Mooseker, M. S. (1976). Brush border motility: microvillar contraction in triton treated brush borders isolated from intestinal epithelium. *J. Cell Biol.* **71**, 417–433.

83. George, E. R., Balakir, R. A., Filburn, C. R. & Sacktor, B. (1977). Cyclic adenosine monophosphate-dependent and -independent protein kinase activity of renal brush border membranes. *Arch. Biochem. Biophys.* **180**, 429–443.

84. Filburn, C. R. & Sacktor, B. (1976). Cyclic nucleotide phosphodiesterases of rabbit renal cortex. *Arch. Biochem. Biophys.* **174**, 249–261.

85. Kinne, R., Shlatz, L. J., Kinne-Saffran, E. & Schwartz, I. L. (1975). Distribution of membrane-bound cyclic AMP-dependent protein kinase in plasma membranes of cells of the kidney cortex. *J. Membr. Biol.* **24**, 145–159.

86. Ishikawa, H., Bischoff, R. & Holtzer, H. (1969). Formation of arrowhead complexes with heavy meromyosin in a variety of cell types. *J. Cell Biol.* **43**, 312–328.

87. Rostgaard, J. & Thuneberg, L. (1972). Electron microscopical observations on the brush border of proximal tubule cells of mammalian kidney. *Z. Zellforsch. Mikrosk. Anat.* **132**, 473–496.

88. Tilney, L. G. & Mooseker, M. (1971). Actin in the brush-border of epithelial cells of the chicken intestine. *Proc. Natl. Acad. Sci. U.S.* **68**, 2611–2615.

89. Booth, A. G. & Kenny, A. J. (1976). Proteins of the kidney microvillus membrane. Identification of subunits after sodium dodecyl sulphate/polyacrylamide-gel electrophoresis. *Biochem. J.* **159**, 395–407.

90. Gabbiani, G., Ryan, G. B., Lamelin, J.-P., Vassalli, P., Majno, G., Bouvier, C. A., Cruchard, A. & Lüscher, E. F. (1973). Human smooth muscle autoantibody: its identification as antiactin antibody and a study of its binding to "non-muscular" cells. *Amer. J. Path.* **72**, 473–488.

91. Schollmeyer, J. V., Goll, D. E., Tilney, L., Mooseker, M., Robson, R. & Stromer, M. (1974). Localization of α-actinin in non muscle material. *J. Cell Biol.* **63**, 304a.

92. Masaki, T., Endo, M. & Ebashi, S. (1967). Localization of 6S component of α-actinin at Z-band. *J. Biochem.* (*Tokyo*) **62**, 630–632.

93. Podlubnaya, Z. A., Tskhovrebova, L. A., Zaalishivili, M. M. & Stefanenko, G. A. (1975). Electron microscopic study of α-actinin. *J. Mol. Biol.* **92**, 357–359.

94. Stossel, T. P. & Hartwig, J. H. (1976). Interactions of actin, myosin, and a new actin-binding protein of rabbit pulmonary macrophages: role in cytoplasmic movement and phagocytosis. *J. Cell Biol.* **68**, 602–619.

95. Wang, K., Ash, J. F. & Singer, S. J. (1975). Filamin, a new high molecular-weight protein found in smooth muscle and non-muscle cells. *Proc. Nat. Acad. Sci. U.S.* **72**, 4483–4486.

96. Tilney, L. G. & Cardell, R. R., Jr. (1970). Factors controlling the reassembly of the microvillous border of the small intestine of the salamander. *J. Cell Biol.* **47**, 408–422.

97. Maestracci, D., Preiser, H., Hedges, T., Schmitz, J. & Crane, R. K. (1975). Enzymes of the human intestinal brush border membrane: identification after gel electrophoretic separation. *Biochim. Biophys. Acta* **382**, 147–156.

98. Critchley, D. R., Howell, K. E. & Eichholz, A. (1975). Solubilization of brush borders of hamster small intestine and fractionation of some of the components. *Biochim. Biophys. Acta* **394**, 361–376.

99. Helenius, A. & Simons, K. (1975). Solubilization of membranes by detergents. *Biochim. Biophys. Acta* **415**, 29–79.

100. Vannier, Ch., Louvard, D., Maroux, S. & Desnuelle, P. (1976). Structural and topological homology between porcine intestinal and renal brush border aminopeptidase. *Biochim. Biophys. Acta* **455**, 185–199.

101. Hughey, R. P. & Carthoys, N. P. (1976). Comparison of the size and physical properties of γ-glutamyl transpeptidase purified from rat kidney following solubilization with papain or with Triton X-100. *J. Biol. Chem.* **251**, 7863–7870.

102. Macnair, R. D. C. & Kenny, A. J. Unpublished work.

103. Semenza, G. (1978). The sucrase-isomaltase complex, a large dimeric amphipathic protein from the small-intestinal brush border membrane: Its positioning and implications as to its biosynthesis. Proceedings of the First Congress of F.A.O.B. (in press).

104. Colbeau, A. & Maroux, S. (1978). Integration of alkaline phosphatase in the intestinal brush border membrane. *Biochim. Biophys. Acta* **511**, 39–51.

105. Maroux, S. & Louvard, D. (1976). On the hydrophobic part of aminopeptidase and maltases which bind the enzyme to the intestinal brush border membrane. *Biochim. Biophys. Acta* **419**, 189–195.
106. Helenius, A. & Simons, K. (1977). Change shift electrophoresis: simple method for distinguishing between amphiphilic and hydrophilic proteins in detergent solution. *Proc. Nat. Acad. Sci. U.S.* **74**, 529–432.
107. Rothman, J. E. & Lenard, J. (1977). Membrane asymmetry: the nature of membrane asymmetry provides clues to the puzzle of how membranes are assembled. *Science* **195**, 743–753.
108. Katz, F. N., Rothman, J. E., Lingappa, V. R., Blobel, G. & Lodish, H. F. (1977). Membrane assembly in vitro: synthesis, glycosylation and asymmetric insertion of a transmembrane protein. *Proc. Nat. Acad. Sci. U.S.* **74**, 3278–3282.
109. Campbell, P. N. & Blobel, G. (1976). The role of organelles in the chemical modification of the primary translation products of secretory proteins. *FEBS Lett.* **72**, 215–226.
110. Louvard, D., Semeriva, M. & Maroux, S. (1976). The brush-border intestinal aminopeptidase, a transmembrane protein as probed by macromolecular photo-labelling. *J. Mol. Biol.* **106**, 1023–1035.
111. Kenny, A. J., Booth, A. G. & Macnair, R. D. C. (1978). Kidney microvillus peptidases—are they transmembrane proteins? In *Biochemical Nephrology* (Güder, W. G. & Schmidt, U., eds) H. Huber Publishers, Bern, Stuttgart, Vienna.
112. Sigrist-Nelson, K., Sigrist, H., Bercovici, T. & Gitler, C. (1977). Intrinsic proteins of the intestinal microvillus: membrane iodonaphthylazide labelling studies. *Biochim. Biophys. Acta* **468**, 163–176.
113. Schulz, S. G. & Curran, P. F. (1970). Coupled transport of sodium and organic solutes. *Physiol. Rev.* **50**, 637–710.
114. Young, J. A. & Freedman, B. S. (1971). Renal tubular transport of amino acids. *Clin. Chem.* **17**, 245–266.
115. Meister, A. (1973). On the enzymology of amino acid transport: transport in kidney and probably other tissues is mediated by a cycle of enzymic reactions involving glutathione. *Science* **180**, 33–39.
116. Meister, A. & Tate, S. S. (1976). Glutathione and related γ-glutamyl compounds: biosynthesis and utilization. *A. Rev. Biochem.* **45**, 449–604.
117. Orlowski, M. & Wilk, S. (1975). Intermediates of the γ-glutamyl cycle in mouse tissues: influence of administration of amino acids on pyrrolidone carboxylate and γ-glutamyl amino acids. *Eur. J. Biochem.* **53**, 581–590.
118. Schulman, J. D., Goodman, S. I., Mace, J. W., Patrick, A. D., Tietze, F. & Butler, E. J. (1975). Glutathionuria: inborn error of metabolism due to tissue deficiency of gamma-glutamyl transpeptidase. *Biochem. Biophys. Res. Commun.* **65**, 68–74.
119. Pellefigue, F., Butler, J. D., Spielberg, S. P., Hollenberg, M. D., Goodman, S. I. & Schulman, J. D. (1976). Normal amino acid uptake by cultured human fibro-blasts does not require gamma-glutamyl transpeptidase. *Biochem. Biophys. Res. Commun.* **73**, 997–1002.
120. Storelli, C., Vögeli, H. & Semenza, G. (1972). Reconstitution of a sucrose-mediated sugar transport system in lipid membranes. *FEBS Lett.* **24**, 287–292.
121. Ramaswamy, K., Malathi, P., Caspary, W. F. & Crane, R. K. (1974). Studies on the transport of glucose from disaccharides by hamster small intestine *in vitro*. *Biochim. Biophys. Acta* **345**, 39–48.

122. Matthews, D. M. (1972). *Rates of Peptide Uptake by Small Intestine in Peptide Transport in Bacteria and Mammalian Gut*, Ciba Foundation symposium. Elsevier North-Holland, pp. 71–92.

123. Crane, R. K., Malathi, P. & Preiser, H. (1976). Reconstitution of specific Na^+-dependent D-glucose transport in liposomes by Triton X-100-extracted proteins from purified brush border membranes of rabbit kidney cortex. *FEBS Lett.* **67**, 214–216.

124. Wacker, H., Müller, F. & Semenza, G. (1976). Incorporation of hydrophobic aminopeptidase from hog kidney into egg lecithin liposomes: number and orientation of aminopeptidase molecules in the lecithin vesicles. *FEBS Lett.* **68**, 145–152.

125. Thuneberg, L. & Rostgaard, J. (1969). Motility of microvilli. *J. Ultrastr. Res.* **29**, 578.

126. Sandström, B. (1971). A contribution to the concept of brush border function. Observations in intestinal epithelium in tissue culture. *Cytobiologie* **3**, 293–297.

127. Rodewald, R., Newman, S. B. & Karnovsky, M. J. (1976). Contraction of isolated brush borders from the intestinal epithelium. *J. Cell Biol.* **70**, 541–554.

128. Maunsbach, A. B. (1966). Absorption of ^{125}I-labelled homologous albumin by rat kidney proximal tubule cells: a study of microperfused single proximal tubules by electron microscopic autoradiography and histochemistry. *J. Ultrastr. Res.* **15**, 197–241.

129. Rodewald, R. (1973). Intestinal transport of antibodies in the newborn rat. *J. Cell Biol.* **58**, 189–211.

130. Williams, K. E., Kidston, E. M., Beck, F. & Lloyd, J. B. (1975). Quantitative studies of pinocytosis: kinetics of protein uptake and digestion by rat yolk sac cultured in vitro. *J. Cell Biol.* **64**, 123–134.

131. Fujita, M., Kawai, K., Asano, S. & Nakao, M. (1973). Protein components of two different regions of an intestinal epithelial cell membrane. Regional singularities. *Biochim. Biophys. Acta* **307**, 141–151.

132. Inoue, S. & Hogg, J. C. (1977). Freeze-etch study of the tracheal epithelium of normal guinea pigs with particular reference to intercellular functions. *J. Ultrastr. Res.* **61**, 89–99.

133. Blouin, A., Bolender, R. P. & Weibel, E. R. (1977). Distribution of organelles and membranes between hepatocytes and nonhepatocytes in the rat liver parenchyma. A stereological study. *J. Cell Biol.* **72**, 441–445.

134. Polliack, A., Lampen, N., Clarkson, B. D., De Harven, E., Bentwich, Z., Siegal, F. P. & Kunkel, H. G. (1973). Identification of human B and T lymphocytes by scanning electron microscopy. *J. Exp. Med.* **138**, 607–624.

135. Gardner, J. D., Brown, M. S. & Laster, L. (1970). The columnar epithelial cell of the small intestine: digestion and transport. *New Engl. J. Med.* **283**, 1196–1202.

136. King, B. F. and Enders, A. C. (1971). Protein absorption by the guinea pig chorioallantoic placenta. *Amer. J. Anat.* **130**, 409–430.

The Neurosecretory Neurone: A Model System for the Study of Secretion

B. T. PICKERING

Department of Anatomy, University of Bristol, Bristol BS8 1TD, England

I. Introduction

"The idea that a nerve cell, or neurone, can secrete a hormone is clearly nonsense." This was the sort of comment made about the concept of neurosecretion when it was first advanced by Ernst Scharrer in 1928[1] and such

45

scepticism persisted well into the 1950s. The theme of this Essay will be not so much a vindication of Scharrer's ideas, because the concept of neurosecretion is now completely accepted (e.g. see references 2, 3, 7) but, rather, I shall go full circle, taking the diametrically opposed view to Scharrer's critics, and suggest that neurones, and particularly neurosecretory neurones, are ideal models for the study of the secretion of proteins and peptides.

Our knowledge of the mechanisms by which proteins destined for export are synthesized by the cell and subsequently secreted is due, largely, to the work of Palade and his colleagues.[4-6] Briefly, the primary synthetic protein is formed on ribosomes attached to the endoplasmic reticulum and passed into the cisternae of this structure. The protein is then translocated to the Golgi area where it is packaged into secretory granules. These granules must then be transported through the cytoplasm of the cell, perhaps to a storage region, and ultimately to the cell periphery so that their contents may be discharged through the cell membrane. For simplicity, it is convenient to consider the whole secretory process to consist of three phases.

1. Synthesis of the molecules to be secreted and their packaging into secretory granules.
2. Transport of these granules from the site of synthesis to the release site.
3. Release, i.e. transfer of the secretory product from inside to outside the cell.

My contention[7] that neurones are good model cells for the study of this process rests on the fact that, in them, these three phases occur in discrete anatomical compartments of the cell. Thus synthesis (which includes the stages which Palade[4] identifies as "synthesis", "segregation", "intracellular transport" and "concentration") takes place largely in the perikaryon, transport in the axon and release occurs predominantly from the nerve terminal.

It is proposed to discuss the contribution of the neurosecretory neurone to our understanding of each of the phases of secretion, but, before beginning, it would seem appropriate to spend a little time introducing the phenomenon of neurosecretion.

II. The Concept of Neurosecretion

A. SECRETORY ACTIVITY OF NEURONES

In 1928 Ernst Scharrer described the occurrence of certain nerve cells, in the hypothalamus of the minnow, which had the appearance of glandular cells[1] and recalled that, some years earlier, Speidel[8] had described similar glandular nerve cells in the spinal cord of the skate. Over the years he and his wife, Berta Scharrer, described many instances of neurosecretory neurones in the central nervous systems of both invertebrates and vertebrates.[9, 10]

The cause of the proponents of neurosecretion received an enormous boost in 1949 when Bargmann[11] examined sections of the brain with a modification of the staining procedure which Gomori had developed for staining the secretory cells of the pancreatic islets. He was able to show the existence of neurones, apparently filled with secretory product, which had their perikarya lying in the supraoptic and paraventricular nuclei of the hypothalamus and

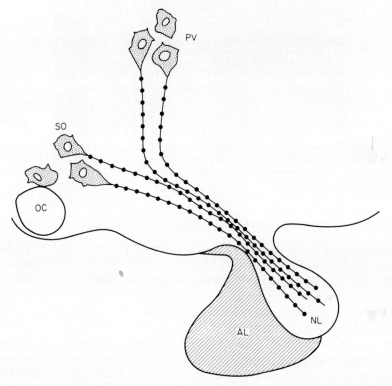

Fig. 1. The hypothalamo-neurohypophysial system. SO: supraoptic nucleus; PV: paraventricular nucleus; AL: anterior lobe; NL: neural lobe of the pituitary gland; OC: optic chiasma.

whose axons left the base of the brain in the pituitary stalk and terminated in the posterior pituitary gland (Fig. 1). Bargmann proposed that the secretory product produced by these nerve cells consisted of the posterior pituitary hormones oxytocin and vasopressin, a suggestion which was substantiated after the electron microscopy studies of Palay[12] had shown the nerve terminals to be packed with secretory granules (Fig. 2) had Lederis & Heller[13] had isolated these granules and shown them to contain the hormones.

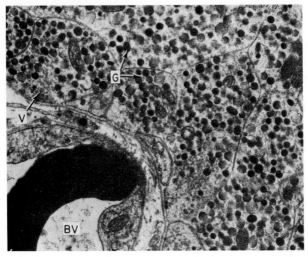

Fig. 2. Electron micrograph (×12,000) of the posterior pituitary gland of the rat showing neuronal dilatations filled with secretory granules (G) in association with a blood vessel (BV). The dilatations contain mitochondria and some, abutting on basement membrane, contain small vesicles (V). (By courtesy of Dr J. F. Morris.)

B. ELECTRICAL ACTIVITY OF NEUROSECRETORY NEURONES

So far, I have briefly outlined the evidence for the presence of secretory cells within the central nervous system—but are they truly nerve cells? In other words, do they propagate and conduct action potentials? Cross & Green[14] recorded action potentials from the supraoptic nucleus of the hypothalamus and found no specialized characteristics, but more precise information could be obtained after Kandel[15] introduced the technique of antidromic identification of neurosecretory neurones. This consists of applying an electrical stimulus to the nerve terminals (e.g. to the posterior pituitary), thus generating an antidromic action potential which travels back up to the cell body and which can be detected by a recording electrode placed in this region (e.g. supraoptic nucleus). In this way one can determine that the cell from which one is recording in the hypothalamus does indeed send an axon to the posterior pituitary, and is thus likely to be a neurosecretory cell. The electrical properties of such identified neurosecretory neurones do not appear to differ from those of ordinary neurones (for review see Cross et al.[16]).

Having established that neurosecretory neurones are both neuronal in the usually accepted sense and secretory, the question remained as to whether these were two separate functions of the cell or integrative components of the cell's activity. Although Cross & Green[14] found that there were changes in the electrical activity of neurones in the supraoptic nucleus in association with stimuli for the release of vasopressin from the posterior pituitary, it was the elegant study of Wakerley & Lincoln[17,18] which clearly related the electrical and secretory activities of these cells. Their findings are summarized in Fig. 3. One of the major physiological functions of the posterior pituitary hormone oxytocin is to cause the let-down of milk from the alveoli of the mammary gland into the teat duct so that it becomes available to the suckled infant. The reflex release of oxytocin from the posterior pituitary gland is stimulated by the presence of the baby on the nipple—a neuroendocrine reflex. In the rat, the young remain attached to the nipple for long periods and during such periods there is a periodic release of oxytocin (about every ten minutes) which, in the anaesthetized animal, can be monitored by recording intramammary pressure through a cannula in one of the teat ducts (Fig. 3). Wakerley & Lincoln[17,18] showed that each of these periodic releases of oxytocin was preceded by a burst of action potentials in about 50% of the neurosecretory neurones travelling from the supraoptic and paraventricular nuclei of the hypothalamus to the posterior pituitary. Moreover, the latent period between the burst of electrical activity and the increase in intramammary pressure equalled the time required for oxytocin, released at the posterior pituitary, to reach and stimulate the myoepithelium in the mammary gland. A similarity between the electrical

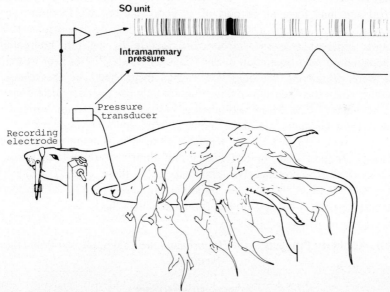

Fig. 3. Scheme for measuring the electrical activity of hypothalamic neurosecretory neurones associated with reflex release of oxytocin during suckling in the rat. The upper trace (supraoptic unit: SO unit) shows the action potentials recorded from a cell in the supraoptic nucleus while the lower trace is a recording of intramammary pressure. Note the burst of potentials which occurs 12 s before the increase in pressure. (By courtesy of Dr D. W. Lincoln.)

activity and hormone release has also been demonstrated for the other neurones in the hypothalamo-neurohypophysial system—those that synthesize and release vasopressin.[19,20] Thus in the neurosecretory neurone the action potentials provide the membrane depolarization which initiates the secretory process at the terminals.

C. NOMENCLATURE—THE ENDOCRINE NEURONE

The definition of neurosecretory neurones has undergone several modifications since their original discovery by Ernst Scharrer. Originally described as neurones full of stainable secretory material, a new definition was required when it became apparent that all neurones were secretory in the elaboration of their neurotransmitters. Knowles & Carlisle[21] suggested that for a neurone to be classed as neurosecretory, it should terminate in a neurohaemal organ and thus discharge its contents into the bloodstream rather than on to the surface of another cell. This definition, however, broke down when it was found that some neurones, which had the ultrastructural appearance of neurosecretory neurones—i.e. were full of secretory granules—made direct contact with endocrine cells. In 1966 Knowles & Bern[22] proposed a modified definition that "neurosecretory neurones are engaged directly or indirectly in endocrine control and may form all or part of an endocrine organ". In recent years, however, this definition, also, has come under considerable strain. It had become apparent (see the introductory lecture to the 6th International Symposium on Neurosecretion by Sir Francis Knowles[23]) that neurosecretory cells were peptidergic neurones (i.e. caused their effects by the release of peptides) and it has been shown now, that not only can peptidergic neurones be seen in synaptic contact one with another but also that they may terminate in areas of the brain apparently quite unrelated to the endocrine system.[24]

The neurones covered by the Knowles & Bern[22] definition represent only one large group of what, by histological and ultrastructural criteria, would be classed as neurosecretory. We prefer to class these cells as "endocrine neurones"[16] and it is to the hypothalamo-neurohypophysial endocrine neurones that I shall confine most of the discussion in this Essay.

III. Secretory Products in the Hypothalamoneurohypophysial Endocrine Neurones

A. THE HORMONES

Since du Vigneaud's success in determining the structures of the mammalian posterior pituitary hormones as nonapeptides in the 1950s,[25] similar nonapeptides have been identified in neurohypophysial extracts from representatives of

Cys Tyr Ile Gln Asn Cys Pro Leu Gly(NH$_2$)

Oxytocin

Cys Tyr Ile Gln Asn Cys Pro Arg Gly(NH$_2$)

[Arg^8]-oxytocin, arginine vasotocin

Cys Tyr Phe Gln Asn Cys Pro Arg Gly(NH$_2$)

[Phe^3, Arg^8]-oxytocin, arginine vasopressin

Cys Tyr Ile Gln Asn Cys Pro Ile Gly(NH$_2$)

[Ile^8]-oxytocin, mesotocin

Cys Tyr Ile Ser Asn Cys Pro Ile Gly(NH$_2$)

[Ser^4, Ile^8]-oxytocin, isotocin

Cys Tyr Ile Ser Asn Cys Pro Gln Gly(NH$_2$)

[Ser^4, Gln^8]-oxytocin, glumitocin

Cys Tyr Ile Asn Asn Cys Pro Leu Gly(NH$_2$)

[Asn^4]-oxytocin, aspargtocin

Cys Tyr Ile Gln Asn Cys Pro Val Gly(NH$_2$)

[Val^8]-oxytocin, valitocin

Fig. 4. Sequences of the vertebrate neurohypophysial hormones.

all the vertebrate classes.[26] These polypeptides represent a series of structural analogues with variations occurring in residues 3, 4 and 8 of the nonapeptide chain (Fig. 4). All of the peptides have a hemicystinyl residue at the amino-terminus and a glycinamide at the carboxyterminus.

Ever since it became apparent that oxytocin and vasopressin are present in the secretory granules in the nerve terminals of the neurohypophysis, efforts have been directed to determine if the hormones are in separate neurones or, at least, separate granules. So far, it has never been possible to isolate vasopressin granules free from oxytocin granules, although there have been several reports that the hormonal granules do tend to separate during density-gradient centrifugation.[28-30]

As Heller[31] pointed out, it would be easier to understand the ability of the posterior pituitary to release the two hormones differentially if each were to be secreted by separate neurones. Arguments for and against the one neurone–one hormone hypothesis have occupied many pages of the literature in the intervening years[32] but the recent introduction of specific immuno-histochemical reactions for the two hormones and their use, particularly by Dierickx and his collaborators have established that one neurone–one hormone is the general rule in the neurohypophysis.

As mentioned earlier (Section II.A) the endocrine neurones of the posterior pituitary have their cell bodies in two distinct hypothalamic nuclei—the supra-optic nucleus (SON) and the paraventricular nucleus (PVN). Early studies[34, 35] suggested that there was a division of labour between these nuclei with SON synthesizing vasopressin and PVN oxytocin. This has now been shown to be unfounded and both nuclei synthesize both hormones.[36, 37]

B. THE NEUROPHYSINS

In 1942 van Dyke and his colleagues[38] showed that all of the biological activities associated with the posterior pituitary (i.e. due to both oxytocin and vasopressin) could be precipitated in the form of an apparently homogeneous protein with a molecular weight of about 30,000. Subsequently, Acher et al.[39] demonstrated that this "van Dyke protein" was an ionic complex between the hormones on the one hand and a so-called inert protein on the other. This inert protein, called neurophysin(e), was later shown to be a family of polypeptides each of which formed stable complexes with the hormones at pH 5·5—complexes which were dissociated at pH values above 7 or below 4.[40] The posterior pituitary is a rich source of peptidases[41] and the neurophysins are readily degraded, giving a falsely high impression of the number of neurophysin species present in a gland, unless the tissue is extracted at pH <1·6 to irreversibly inactivate the degrading enzymes which appear to be of the cathepsin D type.[29] When such precautions are taken, most mammalian posterior pituitary glands are found to contain three neurophysin species of which two are generally present in greater amounts than the third. The polypeptides are usually designated as Neurophysins I, II and III (NpI, NpII, NpIII) according to decreasing electrophoretic mobility.

The neurophysins are stored within the same neurosecretory granules as the hormones[29, 42] and have in the past been considered as carrier molecules necessary to keep the hormones inside the granules during intra-axonal transport.[43] As mentioned above (Section III.A), although oxytocin granules have never been separated from vasopressin ones, they do tend to separate during density-gradient centrifugation. Hope and his colleagues have looked at the neurophysin distribution along such gradients and, using glands from

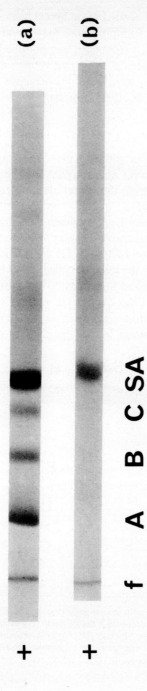

Fig. 5. Polyacrylamide gel electrophoresis of posterior pituitary extracts (a) of a normal rat (b) of a rat which had been drinking 2% NaCl for 5 days prior to death. A, vasopressin-neurophysin (NpI); B, oxytocin-neurophysin (NpII); C, minor neurophysin component (NpIII); SA, serum albumin. Electrophoresis was from right to left (i.e. towards anode).

cattle, found that bovine NpI tended to sediment with oxytocin and bovine NpII with vasopressin,[44] while with pig glands they found that porcine NpI and porcine NpIII sedimented with vasopressin and porcine NpII with oxytocin.[30] In several species, it has also been possible to demonstrate the selective release of one neurophysin component along with one hormone as a result of specific stimuli for the secretion of one or other hormone.[45, 46]

C. NEUROPHYSINS OF THE RAT

When extracts of rat posterior pituitary glands are examined by polyacrylamide gel electrophoresis, the rat neurophysins can be seen as three protein bands with higher mobilities than the serum albumin coming from the blood carried along with the gland (Fig. 5). They can be identified as neurophysins because they: (1) disappear from the gland when the animal is dehydrated (Fig. 5); (2) can be precipitated as an active complex with the hormones by addition of NaCl to a final concentration of 10%;[47] (3) are rich in sulphur as witnessed by the fact that they represent the major labelled bands when glands are taken from animals which have received injections of [^{35}S]cysteine into the cerebrospinal fluid 24 h previously (Fig. 6); (4) are present in the same secretory granules as the hormones.[48] Moreover, when large batches of rat glands were extracted by the classical method for the purification of neurophysins, they

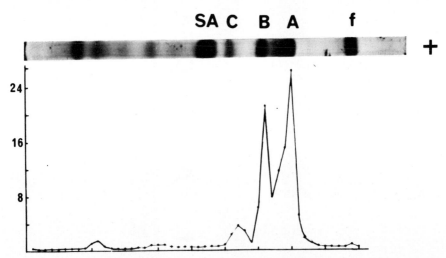

Fig. 6. Association of radioactivity with the rat neurophysin. The animal had received an intracisternal injection of 50 μCi [^{35}S]cysteine 24 h before death. An extract of its posterior pituitary gland was electrophoresed on polyacrylamide gel and, after staining the gel was sliced for the determination of radioactivity. A, vasopressin-neurophysin (NpI); B, oxytocin-neurophysin (NpII); C, minor neurophysin component (NpIII); SA, serum albumin. Electrophoresis was from right to left (i.e. towards anode).

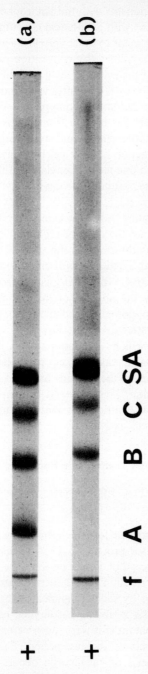

Fig. 7. Polyacrylamide gel electrophoresis of posterior pituitary extracts from Brattleboro rats; (a) heterozygous and (b) homozygous for the disease. A, vasopressin-neurophysin (NpI); B, oxytocin-neurophysin (NpII); C, minor neurophysin component (NpIII); SA, serum albumin. Electrophoresis was from right to left (i.e. towards anode).

were found to yield three components with the electrophoretic mobilities of the three bands shown in Fig. 5 and with amino acid constitutions,[47,49] and partial amino acid sequences,[50] very similar to other vertebrate neurophysins. The two polypeptides with the higher mobilities (by convention rat NpI and rat NpII), and which account for most of the tracer in the glands of labelled animals, can only be resolved one from the other if the buffer used in the polyacrylamide gel electrophoresis system contains sufficient bromophenol blue.[51] This dye, which was added initially as a marker for the ion front, binds to rat NpI to give a complex with a higher net negative charge and thus a higher mobility than rat NpII. The nature of this interaction has not yet been investigated but rat NpI contains one more arginine and one more phenylalanine than rat NpII, both of which residues might play some part in the process.

The first indication that there might be a specific biosynthetic association of one neurophysin for one hormone in the rat came from incorporation studies (Fig. 6) when it was noticed that the ratio of radioactivity associated with rat NpI to that with rat NpII was the same as the ratio of the amounts of vasopressin to oxytocin in the gland.[52] Thus rat NpI could be tentatively designated vasopressin-neurophysin and rat NpII, oxytocin-neurophysin, and such a designation was supported by the absence of rat NpI from rats which were homozygous for hereditary hypothalamic diabetes insipidus (Fig. 7). This strain of rat, known as the Brattleboro strain, was discovered by Valtin and his collaborators; and animals which are homozygous for the disease are completely unable to synthesize vasopressin, while heterozygotes show a reduced amount of the hormone in their glands but can synthesize sufficient to control their water metabolism.[53,54] As can be seen in Fig. 7 the posterior pituitary glands of homozygous Brattleboros contained no rat NpI and heterozygotes showed less rat NpI than rat NpII.

IV. Biosynthesis and Transport in Endocrine Neurones

A. PRECURSORS IN THE BIOSYNTHESIS OF SECRETORY PEPTIDES

Vasopressin was the first hormone for which there was good evidence for the primary synthesis of a precursor protein. In 1964 Sachs and Takabatake[55,56] showed that there was a lag period of $1-1\frac{1}{2}$ h between the administration of the tracer [^{35}S]cysteine and the formation of radioactive vasopressin either by the dog's hypothalamus *in vivo* or by slices of guinea-pig hypothalamus *in vitro*. Moreover, the protein synthesis inhibitor, puromycin, completely suppressed the appearance of labelled hormone if it were given before the tracer but not if it were given towards the end of the lag period. Sachs and Takabatake concluded that "the biosynthesis of vasopressin occurs via the intermediate formation of a precursor molecule which contains the hormone in a bound, biologically inactive form".[56] These conclusions were reached some three years before what is commonly regarded as the first report of a prohormone, proinsulin, by Steiner and his colleagues.[57] It is interesting to note that both Steiner[58] and Sachs[59] reviewed their recent findings at the 1968 Laurentian Hormone Conference.

In the past ten years it has become apparent that many, if not all, polypeptide hormones are synthesized by way of prohormones[60] and, moreover, that even the prohormone is not the primary product of protein synthesis but is also derived from a precursor molecule—the preprohormone[61] which has an additional sequence of hydrophobic residues at the amino terminus. Blobel and his colleagues[61] predicted such "prepeptides", in the biosynthetic pathways for secretory polypeptides, as part of their "signal hypothesis" to explain the translocation of newly synthesized polypeptide into the lumen of the endoplasmic reticulum. There is evidence for the primary synthesis of similar prepeptides in several secretory systems.[62]

B. PARALLEL SYNTHESIS AND TRANSPORT OF THE NEUROHYPOPHYSIAL HORMONES AND THEIR NEUROPHYSINS: A COMMON PRECURSOR?

The arrival of radioactive hormones[63,64] and neurophysins[65,66] in the posterior pituitary after an injection of tracer amino acid into the cerebrospinal fluid has been followed in separate studies. Both classes of polypeptide begin to be labelled in the gland between 1 and $1\frac{1}{2}$ h after the injection of the tracer and there is a parallel increase in the radioactivity associated with each hormone and its neurophysin.

Another indication of this parallel synthesis is obtained from the rates of build-up of the two major neurophysins in the rat gland after an intracisternal injection of [^{35}S]cysteine (Fig. 8). Both vasopressin-neurophysin and oxytocin-neurophysin become labelled in a linear manner during the first 12 h after injection and their rates of increase show a very similar relationship one to the other as the constant ratio of vasopressin to oxytocin stored in the gland. Since the rates at which oxytocin and vasopressin disappear from the gland are the same[64] this constant ratio must be achieved by differential rates of synthesis showing the same relationship to each other as that determined for the two neurophysins.

Studies of the incorporation of radioactivity into neurophysin in the dog, again from Howard Sachs' laboratory,[67] showed that, like vasopressin, this polypeptide is also synthesized by way of a precursor. Moreover, when hypothalamic slices were taken from a dog which had received an infusion of [^{35}S]cysteine into the cerebral ventricles for the previous $1\frac{1}{2}$ h, and incubated *in*

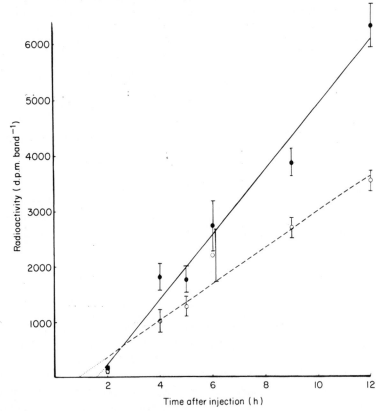

Fig. 8. Build up of radioactivity associated with ●——●, vasopressin-neurophysin (NpI) and ○——○, oxytocin-neurophysin (NpII) in posterior pituitary glands of rats after an intra-cisternal injection of [^{35}S]cysteine (from reference 66).

vitro in the absence of isotope, radioactive hormone and neurophysin appeared in the tissue during the incubation.[67] These findings, taken along with the occurrence of a separate neurophysin for each hormone, and the parallelism in the synthesis of hormones and neurophysins, raise the question of a common precursor for oxytocin and its neurophysin on the one hand and vasopressin and its neurophysin on the other.[47]

More direct evidence for a precursor in neurophysin biosynthesis has come very recently from Gainer and his colleagues.[68, 69] They injected small quantities of a concentrated [^{35}S]cysteine into the brains of rats alongside the supraoptic nuclei and then examined the polypeptides into which this tracer had been incorporated, by electrophoresis on urea-containing polyacrylamide gels under acidic conditions. They found that radioactivity first appeared in a component with a molecular weight of 20,000 and then, as time went on, this species became less labelled as radioactivity appeared in another component which had the same mobility as bovine neurophysin; from the gel, this had an apparent molecular weight of 12,000 (true mol. wt. is 10,000). Both of these components could be precipitated with antibodies directed against rat neurophysin.[70] More refined analysis with isoelectric focusing in poly-acrylamide gel showed Gainer and his colleagues that the "12,000" mol. wt. component was in fact two polypeptides of pI $= 4 \cdot 8$ and $4 \cdot 6$ which were equivalent to our[52] vasopressin-neurophysin and oxytocin-neurophysin. More-over, the "20,000" species was resolvable into four components: pI $6 \cdot 1$, $5 \cdot 6$, $5 \cdot 4$ and $5 \cdot 1$. Two of these (pI $5 \cdot 6$ and $5 \cdot 1$) were somewhat smaller than the other two and, from sodium deodecyl sulphate (SDS)-polyacrylamide gel electrophoresis, had mol. wt. 17,500. The absence of several of the labelled polypeptides (pI $6 \cdot 1$, $5 \cdot 6$, $4 \cdot 8$) from the vasopressin-lacking Brattleboro rats allowed the Gainer group to deduce that these were associated with vaso-pressin biosynthesis, leaving the others to be part of the pathway to oxytocin.[71]

C. THE SIGNIFICANCE OF THE THIRD NEUROPHYSIN IN THE RAT

The discussion in the previous Section IV.B ignored completely the fact that, while there are two posterior pituitary hormones in the rat, there are three neurophysins. Any hypothesis linking the hormones and neurophysins with common precursors must account for this apparent inconsistency.

It became clear from the time-course for the incorporation of radioactive cysteine into the rat neurophysins that the so-called minor neurophysin was labelled with quite different kinetics from the other two (Fig. 9), even though all three neurophysins are found within neurosecretory granules.[48] The rational explanation of these difficulties came from the solution to another dilemma. Even from the curves shown in Fig. 9 it can be seen that the radioactivity in oxytocin-neurophysin falls off more rapidly although it requires a log-linear plot to demonstrate this clearly.[66] Such a difference questions the validity of the identification of the specificity of each neurophysin, as this was based partly on the ratio of radioactivity incorporated into each being the same as the constant ratios of the two hormones stored in the gland. While this equivalence of the two ratios holds for radioactivity measurements within 24 h of injection of the label, the radioactivity ratio of rat NpI to rat NpII gets progressively larger with time. This is even more apparent in the heterozygous Brattleboro rat where the radioactivity ratio inverts (Fig. 10a). The different labelling properties of the rat NpIII (Fig. 9), however, raised the possibility that this polypeptide is a metabolic product of one of the other two arising in the granule after it has arrived in the gland. Such a possibility could be examined by comparing the changes in the radioactivity associated with rat NpI with the sum of the radio-activity associated with rat NpII and rat NpIII. When this was done[66] it was

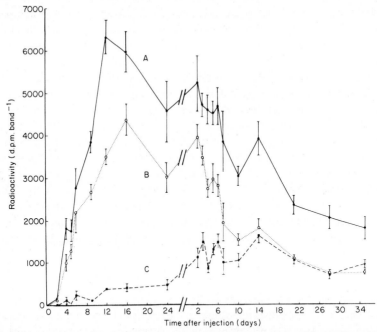

Fig. 9. Change in radioactivity associated with each neurophysin in the rat posterior pituitary gland after an intracisternal injection of [^{35}S]cysteine. A, vasopressin-neurophysin (NpI); B, oxytocin-neurophysin (NpII); C, minor neurophysin component (NpIII) (from reference 47).

found that changes in the sum exactly paralleled concomitant changes in the radioactivity of rat NpI. This is illustrated for the Brattleboro system in Fig. 10b.

More recently, North *et al.*[72] have demonstrated that samples of highly purified rat oxytocin-neurophysin (rat NpII) can be converted into rat NpIII by incubation with posterior pituitary homogenates at pH 4·5. Since, as I have mentioned, all three neurophysins are found within the secretory granules, this implies that the granules contain an enzyme capable of bringing about such a conversion and, indeed, I understand from the authors that North *et al.* have now succeeded in converting rat NpII to rat NpIII with an extract of purified granules at pH 4·5.

I have restricted myself to the consideration of the rat neurophysin because this is the system with which I have been involved personally. However, almost all the species which have been investigated so far have more than two neurophysins alongside two homones.[73] In the pig it has been shown that the minor component (porcine NpIII) is in fact identical with porcine NpI but with an additional three amino acid residues at the carboxy terminus.[74] Just as in the rat there is evidence[75] that conversion occurs as the secretory granule travels

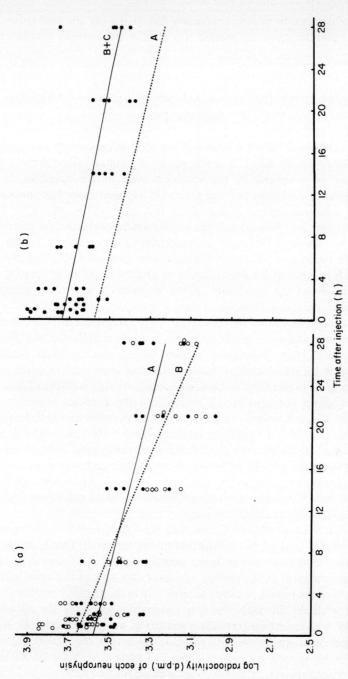

Fig. 10. Decline in radioactivity associated with neurophysins in the heterozygous Brattleboro rat and (b) effect of adding together radioactivity of B and C. A, vasopressin-neurophysin (NpI); B, oxytocin-neurophysin (NpII); C, minor neurophysin component (NpIII).

from hypothalamus to posterior pituitary but in the pig the conversion has gone so far that the metabolic product is present in much greater amounts than its source.

D. WHERE DOES THE PROHORMONE–HORMONE CONVERSION TAKE PLACE?

I mentioned above (Section IV.B and Fig. 9) that radioactive neurophysins and hormones can be detected in the posterior pituitary gland some $1-1\frac{1}{2}$ h after tracer is presented to the synthetic area of the neurones in the hypothalamus. This means that the precursor has been assembled, packaged, processed and transported 3 mm along the axon within this time. Even allowing no time for synthesis etc. this implies a minimum transport velocity of $3-4$ mm h^{-1} which is the rapid transport class for neurones.[63] Taking into account the findings of Sachs and his colleagues (Section IV.A) that approximately $1\frac{1}{4}$ h is required for the assembly of precursor and its processing into vasopressin, either the movement of the granules is very rapid indeed or processing of precursor must occur during transport. Some evidence for the latter possibility has existed for some time: Vogt pointed out in 1953[76] that the different vasopressin to oxytocin ratios found for hypothalamus and gland in all the species then investigated implied either that oxytocin could be synthesized in the gland itself or that it arose from some inactive precursor en route from brain to pituitary. In his first experiments Howard Sachs found that secretory granules prepared from hypothalamus of pre-infused dogs contained vasopressin of much lower specific radioactivity than the hormone present in granules isolated from the posterior pituitary gland.[77] He concluded that these findings were compatible with the formation of vasopressin from an inactive precursor inside the granule on its way from perikaryon to the axon terminal. The later finding of intragranular conversion of neurophysins (Section IV.C) shows that there is at least one protease present inside the granule so that such precursor processing could occur there.

The recent work of Harold Gainer and his colleagues[68, 69, 71] has provided more convincing evidence for conversion during transport. One hour after an injection of [^{35}S]cysteine alongside the perikarya in the SON there is no radioactivity demonstrable in the median eminence (an area of the hypothalamus which contains the bundle of axons on their way to the posterior pituitary) or in the gland itself. In the SON the only radioactive species is the apparently 20,000 mol. wt. component (actually a mixture as we saw in Section IV.B). By 2 h, the median eminence contains radioactivity both in the 20,000 and in the 12,000 mol. wt. species in a ratio of about 2:3 while in SON the 20,000 is still the predominant species. Since the material in the median eminence at 2 h must

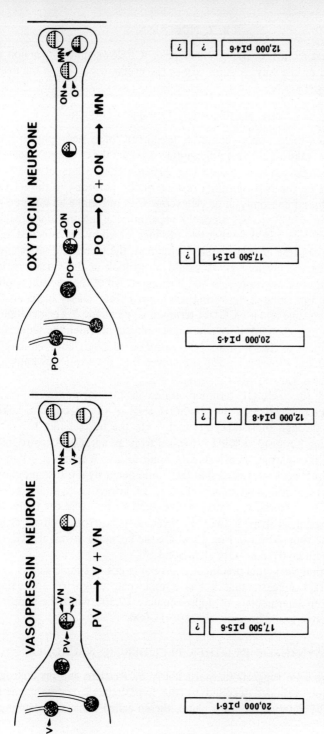

Fig. 11. Scheme for maturation in the neurohypophysial neurone of the rat shown together with the intermediates identified by Gainer & Brownstein.[71] ? represents the as yet unidentified peptides but includes the hormones, PV, provasopressin; V, vasopressin; PO, pro-oxytocin; ON, oxytocin-neurophysin (NpI); NpII, minor neurophysin component (NpIII); MN, minor neurophysin component (NpIII); O, oxytocin.

have originated from the SON 20,000 peak it follows that conversion must have occurred on the way. A summary of the events occurring in the neurone is shown in Fig. 11.

E. THE NATURE OF THE PRECURSOR

The simplest form that a common precursor for a neurophysin and its hormone could take would be a polypeptide in which the two components were linked by a single covalent bond. The question then arises of whether the linkage would be the NH_2-terminal residue of the hormone to the $-COOH$-terminal residue of neurophysin or vice versa. Can one make an inspired guess at which way it is likely to be? Since the maturation of the precursor requires a proteolytic cleavage it is likely that two residues joined by the attached peptide bond will be the same or very similar throughout the vertebrate series and one way of making the inspired guess would be to look at the variations in the terminal residues of neurophysins and hormones. All of the neurohypophysial hormones so far isolated (covering each vertebrate class) have an NH_2-terminal hemicystine and a $-COOH$-terminal glycinamide.[78] The neurophysins are not much more helpful, since every neurophysin of which the sequence has been determined so far has an NH_2-terminal alanine, and, although the $-COOH$-terminal shows more variation, even then the sequences known vary only among Leu, Val and Ala.[73]

Because of the $-COOH$-terminal amide in the hormones, it has been suggested that they arise as the $-COOH$ ends of the precursors, linked to neurophysin through their NH_2-terminal.[79] On the other hand, the melano-cyte-stimulating hormone α-MSH is formed from an adrenocorticotrophin-like precursor by the splitting of a Val$-$Gly bond to give a terminal $-Val(NH_2)$. Bradbury et al.[80] have suggested that this could occur by a transamidation-like reaction from an ammonia donor. This is an attractive hypothesis for the formation of the several, amidated, active peptides found in the body. In the neurohypophysial system it would mean a precursor with a structure somewhat like that shown in Fig. 12 where the hormone terminal $-Gly(NH_2)$ would be generated from a $-Gly-Ala$ bond.[7, 81]

We know that the actual precursor is probably not as simple as this because Gainer's work[71] suggests that it has a molecular weight of approximately 20,000 with an intermediate of approximately 17,500 while the simple form referred to above would be approximately 11,000.

F. SYNTHESIS IN OTHER PEPTIDERGIC NEURONES

There have been suggestions, particularly by Reichlin and his colleagues,[82] that the active peptides secreted by the hypothalamic endocrine neurones controlling the anterior pituitary gland, the so-called releasing hormones, are

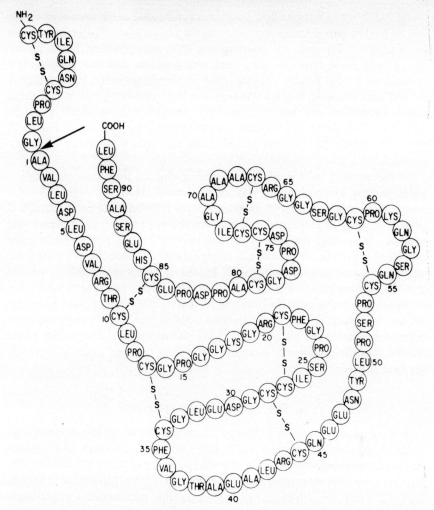

Fig. 12. A hypothetical intermediate between bovine pro-oxytocin and neurophysin plus oxytocin. The arrow identifies the bond which would be attacked by the transamidase suggested by Bradbury et al.[80]

synthesized by soluble enzymes without recourse to ribosomes. Reichlin's work pointed to the existence of a series of synthetases which were apparently capable of bringing about an ATP-dependent conjugation of the amino acids not only in the synthesis of the tripeptide thyrotrophin-releasing hormone (TRH) but also the decapeptide luteinizing hormone-releasing hormone (LRH).[82] These hormones are known to be stored in similar dense-cored granules to those of the posterior pituitary hormones[83,84] and I have always found it difficult to imagine how hormones synthesized in the axonal terminals can be packed into granules arriving from the perikaryon.[7,16] My criticism can be countered, however, by pointing out that noradrenaline taken up by sympathetic nerve terminals goes back into granules, and that acetylcholine synthesized by the soluble enzyme, choline acetyltransferase, is nevertheless packed into synaptic vesicles. Perhaps the best answer to this is that these active substances are not peptides—the proteinaceous products of these adrenergic and cholinergic systems are the synthesizing enzymes and some of these do appear to be transported from the perikarya within secretory granules.[7]

At the moment there is no direct evidence that the hypothalamic-releasing hormones are synthesized by way of precursors. However, high molecular weight forms which react with antibodies to the hormones are being found.[85,86] Moreover, there is increasing evidence for the presence of other peptidergic neurones throughout the central nervous system,[87] and it would appear to be the rule that their neuropeptides e.g. enkaphalins[88] and endorphins[89] arise from larger molecular weight precursors.[90] Indeed, it seems reasonable to predict that all neuropeptides will be found to arise from precursors which are packaged into granules in the neuronal perikarya, and finally processed during axonal transport in the way described above for the neurohypophysial hormones. Gainer and his colleagues have shown a similar mechanism in the formation of the products of some neurosecretory neurones in the invertebrate sea hare (Aplysia).[91]

G. THE MODE OF TRANSPORT

In have already mentioned (Section IV.B) that hormones and neurophysins inside their secretory granules are transported along the axons of the hypothalamoneurohypophysial tract at velocities in excess of 3 mm h^{-1} and that this puts them into the class of substances which are rapidly transported in nerves. Dahlström and her colleagues had first shown that noradrenaline granules are rapidly transported in sympathetic neurones[92,93] and more recently have found similar velocities for some acetylcholine vesicles in cholinergic neurones.[94] The observation that these rapid transport systems are inhibited by mitotic poisons such as colchicine and vinblastine,[95] which inhibit the polymerization of tubulin,[96] led F. O. Schmitt[97,98] to advance his sliding vesicle hypothesis for neuronal transport. This concept is a direct analogy with Huxley & Hanson's[99] sliding filament hypothesis for muscle contraction, for Schmitt[98] visualizes that just as in muscle the myosin subunits slide along the actin filaments, so in the neurone, the vesicle would slide along the tubulin of the neurotubule. To complete the analogy the system would require a nucleotide (ATP or GTP) and a nucleotidase but there are conflicting reports about whether these components are present, as they would need to be, in the membrane of neuronal secretory granules.[100,101]

Certainly granule transport in the hypothalamo-neurohypophysial endocrine neurones appears to be inhibited by colchicine according to both morphological studies with the electron microscope[102] and to biochemical studies measuring the rate of arrival of radioactive neurophysin after injection of [^{35}S]cysteine into SON.[103] This effect is not all-or-none, since my colleague, David Parish, (cited in reference 104) has demonstrated a dose-dependent inhibition by colchicine of the arrival of the individual rat neurophysins in the posterior pituitary glands. Doses as low as 3 μg per animal will reduce, by 50%, the amount of newly synthesized neurophysin arriving in the gland in a 24 h period following tracer injection.

At present there is no real, solid evidence linking granular transport with neurotubules, but Schmitt's hypothesis[97,98] remains the most attractive available. Moreover, Grainger & Sloper[105] have described hypothalamo-neurohypophysial neurones in the Brattleboro rat (a strain unable to synthesize vasopressin) filled with neurotubules. They have suggested that these represent "frustrated neurones" maximally stimulated to transport and release the non-existent vasopressin-containing granules.

V. Storage and Release

The neurohypophysial hormones, along with their associated neurophysins, are stored inside the neurosecretory granules within dilatations of the axons in the posterior pituitary. Indeed the posterior pituitary is largely composed of such axonal dilatations, each axon entering the gland having many hundreds of them, themselves varying tremendously in size.[106] The larger ones are readily visible with the light microscope and were described by Herring[107] in 1908 and have subsequently been known as Herring bodies.

In this section I shall consider the distribution of the granules within the axonal storage areas—is it random or is there a predetermined route for the granules to take? I shall also discuss the mode of release for the granules and, although it is perhaps somewhat illogical, I will begin with this.

A. THE MODE OF RELEASE—EXOCYTOSIS OR DIFFUSION?

In their description of secretory events in the pancreatic exocrine cell, Palade and his colleagues have described the fusion of secretory granules with the cell membrane and the discharge of their contents into the lumen of the duct.[4] This process of exocytosis has been documented for many polypeptide secreting systems as well as for the release of transmitter substances by neurones. The posterior pituitary hormones are no exception to this general rule but it has taken many years to reach agreement about this. The evidence that posterior pituitary hormones are released by exocytosis has been reviewed on a number of occasions; notably by W. W. Douglas[108,109] and J. J. Dreifuss[110,111] and rests largely on the finding of parallel release of hormone and neurophysin[112,113] in the absence of a concomitant release of lactic dehydrogenase.[114] It is also possible to demonstrate, though rarely, exocytotic images in the electron microscope[115] and much more readily by the use of the technique of freeze fracture.[111,116]

B. RECAPTURE OF GRANULE MEMBRANE AFTER RELEASE

When secretory product is released by the process of exocytosis there is a fusion of the membrane of the secretory granule with the plasmalemma[4] which thus increases in surface area. In the rat neurohypophysis 5% of the product turns over each day[64] and, since the gland contains 2×10^{10} granules,[117] this would mean that the membranes of 10^9 granules become incorporated into the axonal membranes each day. Clearly there has to be some mechanism for removing an equivalent amount of membrane so that secretory cells maintain their size. Norman[118] studying neurosecretion in an insect observed an increase in the number of so-called microvesicles in the axon terminals after stimulation of hormone release, and suggested that these vesicles represented recaptured membrane. Douglas and his co-workers[119] proposed a similar membrane-recapture mechanism in the posterior pituitary gland, which also contains microvesicles (see Fig. 2), and suggested that, after exocytosis, the membrane of the late granule is retrieved by pinocytosis of microvesicles. Support for this suggestion came from claims that there was an increase in microvesicle numbers correlated with increased release,[120] although more recently, Nordmann & Morris[121] have shown that this apparent increase is not a real one but comes about from an intracellular redistribution of microvesicles so that they come to lie closer to the limiting membrane.

Certainly, freeze-fracture studies show that there is endocytosis associated with exocytosis[116] but is the membrane endocytosed in the form of small vesicles? In a study of secretion-related uptake of extracellular markers, Nordmann et al.[122] found that greater volumes of extracellular fluid were taken up than would be expected from the relatively high surface area to volume ratios of small vesicles. Moreover, using horseradish peroxidase, they found evidence of endocytosis of large vacuoles comparable in size to the original secretory granules. Similar vacuoles have also been described by Castel.[123] Further doubts that the microvesicles represent the simple product of granule-membrane endocytosis came from a completely different approach in our laboratory. We were able to label the membranes of the hormone granules in the rat posterior pituitary gland by injecting [³H]choline intracisternally. We

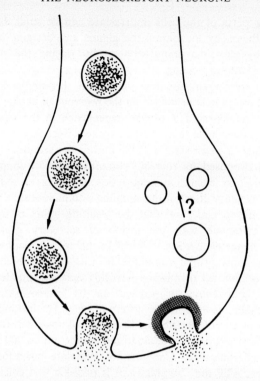

Fig. 13. Scheme for retrieval of granule membrane.

prepared subcellular fractions of the glands of injected rats at various times (from 2 h to 4 weeks) after injection and expected to see a gradual shift of the tracer from the granule-membrane fraction to the fraction (microsomal) which contained the microvesicles. This did not occur and, moreover, when we brought about massive hormonal release ($>$80%) by allowing the injected animals to drink 2% NaCl instead of water for 5 days we found that the tracer was returned in the centrifugal fraction equivalent to the granule membranes.[48] Thus our results, too, are compatible with the membrane of an exocytosed granule being recaptured in the form of a vacuole having similar dimensions to the original granule and allow us to propose the scheme shown in Fig. 13.

C. MECHANISM FOR RELEASE

The great advantage of the posterior pituitary is that the gland represents purely a storage and release system, being composed solely of the axon terminals which are unable to synthesize new product. When the gland is removed by cutting the pituitary stalk, these storage organs are separated from the synthesizing parts of the cells and release can be studied *in vitro* in the absence of synthesis, by incubating the glands and bringing about hormone release either by electrical stimulation or by raising the potassium concentration of the bathing medium.

Following on from their studies with adrenal chromaffin cells[124] in which they showed an absolute dependence on the presence of calcium, Douglas and his colleagues demonstrated a similar dependence in the neurohypophysial system[109, 125] as indeed have several other workers since then.[111, 126] Many other systems also show a necessity for Ca^{2+} during the secretory process[109] and Douglas[127] has proposed its role in "stimulus-secretion coupling" as being analogous to that in excitation–contraction coupling in muscle. It would appear that the primary effect of the stimulus is to increase the permeability of the cell membrane to Ca^{2+} and that the resulting influx of this ion initiates events which culminate with the fusion of secretory granules with the membrane and hence exocytosis.[109, 111, 126] In the neurohypophysial system, as in many others, this primary increase in Ca^{2+} permeability results from depolarization of the cell membrane and this may be initiated by electrical activity, either endogenous or applied, or by increasing the potassium concentration of the medium in the system *in vivo*. The mechanism, by which Ca^{2+} brings about granule-membrane fusion is unknown but there must be at least two phases: transport of granule to membrane and actual fusion. Since it has been claimed that while Ca^{2+} cannot stimulate hormone release from isolated granules, ATP may be able to, it is possible that calcium's role is in connection with a membrane ATPase.[128] However, as has been mentioned in Section IV.G, evidence about the occurrence of such an enzyme in granule membranes is conflicting, and it is perhaps wise to defer further comment until more information about the events immediately preceding exocytosis become clearer; for these studies, the isolated neurohypophysis would make a good test system.

D. THE DISTRIBUTION OF SECRETORY GRANULES IN THE STORES—RANDOM OR ORDERED?

In a "conventional" secretory cell there is a mixture of granules: those which are in the process of being formed in the Golgi area, those which are being stored and those ready for, or in the act of, being released. The posterior pituitary gland is somewhat simpler since all of the granules it contains are fully formed, and have been transported along the axons from the synthetic areas in the perikaryon. The question I wish to discuss here is: Do the axonal dilatations in the gland contain a homogeneous mixture of these granules, or is there some predetermined route which a granule takes through a cell?

Indications that the gland does not contain a homogeneous mixture of hormone granules came from the observation of Sachs and his colleagues that hormone released either *in vivo* or *in vitro* from the gland of a dog which had received an intraventricular infusion of [^{35}S]cysteine 10 days previously, had a higher specific radioactivity than the total hormone stored in the gland.[67] When we[129] repeated this study in the rat we found that while 20% of the labelled neurophysin could be released *in vitro* by stimulating glands taken from animals 4 h after injection of tracer, this proportion fell off as time between injection and assessment increased, to reach 5% at 21 days. This proportion (5%) was equivalent to the fraction of total neurophysin which was released from glands taken at any time after injection. In other words our results, together with those of Sachs[67] and of Norström,[130] suggested that granules released in response to a stimulus contain a far greater proportion of newly synthesized product than would be expected if the pool of granules available for release were homogeneous.

A concept of a "readily releasable" pool of hormone grew up from studies in the laboratories of both Sachs[59, 131] and Thorn.[132] They found that glands stimulated either *in vivo* or *in vitro* could release up to 10% of their stored hormone, but that a second stimulus was ineffective unless a considerable period was allowed to elapse between stimuli. The results discussed in the previous paragraph suggest that the newly synthesized granules enter the "readily releasable" pool before reaching the storage pool, and are compatible with a predetermined route for granules. More recent studies[133, 134] have suggested that the "readily releasable" pool is apparent rather than real, and arises from limitations on Ca^{2+} movement across the membranes. Nevertheless, the evidence that more newly synthesized material is released preferentially still stands and, indeed, seems to be true for other secretory systems as well.[135-137]

One of the suggestions put forward by Sachs and his colleagues as a possible explanation for the existence of a "readily releasable" pool was that it arises from the "spatial orientation [of hormone] within the axon (e.g. only those neurosecretory granules in close apposition to the neuronal membranes in the nerve terminals can discharge their contents into the perivascular space)".[138] In order to test this hypothesis we took advantage of our findings[47] that most of the radioactivity which arrives in the gland after an intracisternal injection of [^{35}S]cysteine is associated with hormones or neurophysins i.e. with the contents of neurosecretory granules. We gave rats intracisternal injections of the isotope and then prepared glands, taken from rats at various times after the injection, for electron microscope radioautoradiography.[139] Our findings, which are summarized in Fig. 14, showed that radioactive granules arriving along the axons to reach the axonal dilatations were first found in small dilatations which contain the microvesicles referred to earlier (Section V.B) and which also abut

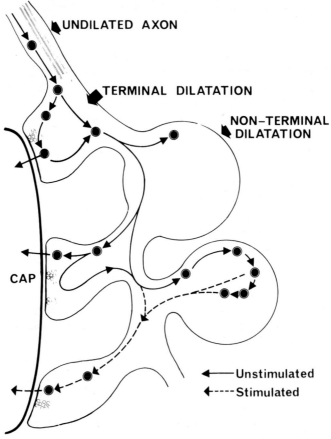

Fig. 14. Scheme for the movement of neurosecretory granules through the compartments of the hypothlamo-neurohypophysial neurone within the neural lobe of the pituitary gland. CAP, blood capillary (from reference 139).

on basement membrane[140]—these we arbitrarily called "nerve endings". The granules then appeared to move into larger dilatations (which we called "nerve swellings") and, indeed moved deeper and deeper into progressively larger and larger swellings.

This evidence strongly suggests that granules move along a predetermined route from the synthesis site directly to release site and thence, for those which escape release, to the storage site. This would explain why newly synthesized hormone is preferentially released and might be a general phenomenon in secretory cells. Teleologically such a system is good sense since it means that, under conditions of extreme need, the product is available for release as rapidly as possible and is only shunted into "store" when the need subsides.

How can the predetermined route be defined? Clearly a simple way, if microtubules are related to granular transport, would be by a microtubular "railway" connecting granule production sites (Golgi) to storage areas via release sites. Since a store is only of use if its contents can be called upon and, indeed, there is evidence that neurohypophysial stores can be emptied in response to severe stimuli, such as dehydration,[141] it must be possible for two-way traffic to occur along some sections of the "railway".

VI. General Concluding Remarks

I have attempted to show that all of the phases usually associated with the secretion of proteins occur within the endocrine neurones whose axonal endings constitute the posterior pituitary gland. My claim that this represents a good model system for the study of secretion in general rests on the fact that the shape of the cell allows the dissection of different phases of secretion which occur in different anatomical compartments. The development of long-term organ culture systems for intact hypothalamo-neurohypophysial systems[142, 143] offers great hope that this model can be studied *in vitro* to provide answers to some of the remaining enigmas such as the nature of the granule transporting mechanism and the sequence of events immediately preceding exocytosis.

ACKNOWLEDGEMENTS

I am grateful to all my colleagues, past and present, who have willingly given advice, provided illustrative material and acted as sounding boards during the preparation of this Essay. Experimental work in our laboratory has been supported by grants from the Royal Society and the Medical Research Council as well as by the able technical assistance of a number of people but especially of Hazel Searle.

REFERENCES

1. Scharrer, E. (1928). Die Lichtempfindlicheit blinder Elritzen. (Untersuchungen über das Zwischenhirn der Fische I.) Z. Vgl. Physiol. 7, 1–38.
2. Bern, H. A. & Knowles, F. G. W. (1966). Neurosecretion. In Neuro-endocrinology Vol. 1 (Martini, L. & Ganong, W. F., eds). Academic Press, New York and London, pp. 136–186.
3. Scharrer, B. (1976). Neurosecretion—comparative and evolutional aspects. Progr. Brain Res. 45, 125–137.
4. Palade, G. (1975). Intracellular aspects of protein synthesis. Science 189, 347–358.
5. Jamieson, J. D. & Palade, G. E. (1967). Intracellular transport of secretory proteins in the pancreatic exocrine cell. I. Role of the peripheral elements of the Golgi complex. J. Cell Biol. 34, 577–596.

6. Jamieson, J. D. & Palade, G. E. (1967). Intracellular transport of secretory proteins in the pancreatic endocrine cell. II. Transport to condensing vacuoles and zymogen granules. *J. Cell Biol.* **34**, 597–615.

7. Pickering, B. T. (1976). The molecules of neurosecretion: their formation, transport and release. *Progr. Brain Res.* **45**, 161–179.

8. Spiedel, C. G. (1919). Gland cells of internal secretion in the spinal cord of the skates. *Carnegie Inst. Wash. Publ.* **13**, 1–31.

9. Scharrer, E. & Scharrer, B. (1945). Neurosecretion. *Physiol. Rev.* **25**, 171–181.

10. Scharrer, E. & Scharrer, B. (1954). Neurosekretion. In *Handbuch der mikroskopischen Anatomie des Menschen*, Vol. 6 (Möllendorf, W. & Bargmann, W., eds). Springer, Berlin, pp. 953–1066.

11. Bargmann, W. (1949). Über die neurosekretorische Verknüpfung von Hypothalamus und Neurohypophyse. *Z. Zellforsch. Mikrosk. Anat.* **34**, 610–634.

12. Palay, S. L. (1957). In *Ultrastructure and Cellular Chemistry of Neural Tissue* (Waelsch, H., ed.). Hoeber, New York, pp. 31–49.

13. Lederis, K. & Heller, H. (1960). Intracellular storage of vasopressin and oxytocin in the posterior pituitary lobe. *Acta Endocr.* (*Copenh.*) **Suppl. 51**, 115–116.

14. Cross, B. A. & Green, J. D. (1959). Activity of single neurones in the hypothalamus: effect of osmotic and other stimuli. *J. Physiol.* (*London*) **148**, 554–569.

15. Kandel, E. R. (1964). Electrical properties of hypothalamic neuroendocrine cells. *J. Gen. Physiol.* **47**, 691–717.

16. Cross, B. A., Dyball, R. E. J., Dyer, R. G., Jones, C. W., Lincoln, D. W., Morris, J. F. and Pickering, B. T. (1975). Endocrine neurones. *Rec. Progr. Horm. Res.* **31**, 243–294.

17. Wakerley, J. B. & Lincoln, D. W. (1973). The milk-ejection reflex of the rat: a 20- to 40-fold acceleration in the firing of paraventricular neurones during the release of oxytocin. *J. Endocr.* **57**, 477–493.

18. Lincoln, D. W. & Wakerley, J. B. (1974). Electrophysiological evidence for the activation of supraoptic neurones during the release of oxytocin. *J. Physiol.* (*London*) **242**, 533–554.

19. Harris, M. C., Dreiffus, J. J. & Legros, J. J. (1975). Excitation of phasically firing supraoptic neurones during vasopressin release. *Nature* (*London*) **258**, 80–82.

20. Wakerley, J. B., Poulain, D. A., Dyball, R. E. J. & Cross, B. A. (1975). Activity of phasic neurosecretory cells during haemorrhage. *Nature* (*London*) **258**, 82–84.

21. Knowles, F. G. W. & Carlisle, D. B. (1956). Endocrine control in crustacea. *Biol. Rev.* **31**, 396–473.

22. Knowles, F. G. W. & Bern, H. A. (1966). The function of neurosecretion in endocrine regulation. *Nature* (*London*) **210**, 271–272.

23. Knowles, F. (1974). Twenty years of neurosecretion. In *Neurosecretion—the Final Neuroendocrine Pathway* (Knowles, F. & Volkrath, L., eds). Berlin, Springer-Verlag, pp. 3–11.

24. Swanson, L. W. (1977). Immunohistochemical evidence for a neurophysin-containing autonomic pathway arising in the paraventricular nucleus of the hypothalamus. *Brain Res.* **128**, 346–353.

25. Du Vigneaud, V. (1956). Hormones of the posterior pituitary gland: Oxytocin and vasopressin. *The Harvey Lectures* **50**, 1–26.

26. Heller, H. & Pickering, B. T. (1970). The distribution of vertebrate neuro-

hypophysial hormones and its relation to possible pathways for their evolution. In *Intl. Encyclopedia Pharmacol. Ther.* Sect. 41 (Heller, H. & Pickering, B. T., eds). Pergamon Press, Oxford, pp. 59–79.

27. Barer, R., Heller, H. & Lederis, K. (1963). The isolation, identification and properties of the hormonal granules of the neurohypophysis. *Proc. R. Soc. B.* **158**, 388–416.

28. LaBella, F. S., Reiffenstein, R. J. & Beaulieu, G. (1963). Subcellular fractionation of bovine posterior pituitary glands by centrifugation. *Arch. Biochem. Biophys.* **100**, 399–408.

29. Dean, C. R. & Hope, D. B. (1967). The isolation of purified neurosecretory granules from bovine pituitary posterior lobes. Comparison of granule protein constituents with those of neurophysin. *Biochem. J.* **104**, 1082–1088.

30. Pickup, J. C., Johnston, C. I., Nakamura, S., Uttenthal, L. O. & Hope, D. B. (1973). Subcellular organization of neurophysins, oxytocin, (8-lysine)-vasopressin and adenosine triphosphatase in porcine posterior pituitary lobes. *Biochem. J.* **132**, 361–371.

31. Heller, H. (1966). The hormone content of the vertebrate hypothalamo-neurohypophysial system. *Br. Med. Bull.* **22**, 227–231.

32. Morris, J. F., Sokol, H. & Valtin, H. (1977). One neuron—one hormone? Recent evidence from Brattleboro rats. In *The Neurohypophysis* (Moses, A. M. & Share, L., eds). Basle, Karger, pp. 58–66.

33. Dierickx, K., Vandesande, F. & Goossens, N. (1978). The one-neuron-one-hormone hypothesis and the hypothalamic magnocellular neurosecretory system of the vertebrates. In *La Biologie Cellulaire des Processus Neurosécretoires Hypothalamiques* (Vincent, J. D., ed.) (in press).

34. Nibbelinck, D. W. (1961). Paraventricular nuclei, neurohypophysis and parturition. *Amer. J. Physiol.* **200**, 1229–1232.

35. Olivecrona, H. (1957). Paraventricular nucleus and pituitary gland. *Acta Physiol. Scand.* **40**, *Suppl. 136*, 1–178.

36. Burford, G. D., Dyball, R. E. J., Moss, R. L. & Pickering, B. T. (1974). Synthesis of both neurohypophysial hormones in both the paraventricular and supraoptic nuclei of the rat. *J. Anat.* **117**, 261–269.

37. Vandesande, F., Dierickx, K. & DeMey, J. (1975). Identification of the vasopressin-neurophysin II and the oxytocin-neurophysin I producing neurons in the bovine hypothalamus. *Cell Tiss. Res.* **156**, 189–200.

38. Van Dyke, H. B., Chow, B. F., Greep, R. O. & Rothen, A. (1942). Isolation of a protein from the pars neuralis of the ox pituitary with constant oxytocic pressor and diuresis-inhibiting activities. *J. Pharmacol. Exp. Ther.* **74**, 190–209.

39. Acher, R., Manoussos, G. & Olivry, G. (1955). Sur les rélations entre l'ocytocine et la vasopressine d'une part et la protéine de van Dyke d'autre part. *Biochim. Biophys. Acta* **16**, 155–156.

40. Ginsburg, M. & Ireland, M. (1964). Binding of vasopressin and oxytocin to protein in extracts of bovine and rabbit neurohypophyses. *J. Endocr.* **30**, 131–145.

41. Ellis, S. (1961). Studies in the serial extraction of pituitary proteins. *Endocrinology* **69**, 554–570.

42. Ginsburg, M. & Ireland, M. (1966). The role of neurophysin in the transport and release of neurohypophysial hormones. *J. Endocr.* **35**, 289–298.

43. Sawyer, W. H. (1961). Neurohypophyseal Hormones. *Pharmacol. Rev.* **13**, 225–277.

44. Dean, C. R., Hope, D. B. & Kažić, T. (1968). Evidence for the storage of oxytocin with neurophysin I and of vasopressin with neurophysin II in separate neurosecretory granules. *Br. J. Pharmacol.* **34**, 192–193P.

45. Robinson, A. G. (1975). Utilization of specific neurophysin assays to demonstrate independent secretion of different neurophysins *in vivo*. *Ann. N.Y. Acad. Sci.* **248**, 246–256.

46. Legros, J. J. (1975). The radioimmunoassay of human neurophysins: contribution to the understanding of the physiopathology of neurohypophyseal function. *Ann. N.Y. Acad. Sci.* **248**, 281–303.

47. Pickering, B. T., Jones, C. W., Burford, G. D., McPherson, M., Swann, R. W., Heap, P. F. & Morris, J. F. (1975). The role of neurophysin proteins: suggestions from the study of their transport and turnover. *Ann. N.Y. Acad. Sci.* **248**, 15–35.

48. Swann, R. W. & Pickering, B. T. (1976). Incorporation of radioactive precursors into the membrane and contents of the neurosecretory granules of the rat neurohypophysis as a method of studying their fate. *J. Endocr.* **68**, 95–108.

49. North, W. G. & Valtin, H. (1977). The purification of rat neurophysins by a method of preparative polyacrylamide gel electrophoresis. *Analyt. Biochem.* **78**, 436–450.

50. Schlesinger, D. H., Pickering, B. T., Watkins, W. B., Peek, J. C., Moore, L. G., Audhya, T. K. and Walter, R. (1977). A comparative study of partial neurophysin protein sequences of cod, guinea pig, rat and sheep. *FEBS Lett.* **80**, 371–373.

51. Burford, G. D. & Pickering, B. T. (1972). The number of neurophysins in the rat. Influence of the concentration of bromophenol blue, used as a tracking dye, on the resolution of protein by polyacrylamide-gel electrophoresis. *Biochem. J.* **128**, 941–944.

52. Burford, G. D., Jones, C. W. & Pickering, B. T. (1971). Tentative identification of a vasopressin-neurophysin and an oxytocin-neurophysin in the rat. *Biochem. J.* **124**, 809–813.

53. Valtin, H. (1967). Hereditary hypothalamic diabetes insipidus in rats (Brattleboro strain). A useful experimental model. *Amer. J. Med.* **42**, 814–827.

54. Valtin, H., Stewart, J. & Sokol, H. (1974). Genetic control of the production of posterior pituitary principles. In *The Pituitary Gland and its Control*, Handbook of Physiology, Sect. 7, Vol. IV., Part I (Knobil, E. & Sawyer, W. H., eds). American Physiological Society, Washington, D.C., pp. 131–171.

55. Takabatake, Y. & Sachs, H. (1964). Vasopressin biosynthesis III *in vitro* studies. *Endocrinology* **75**, 934–942.

56. Sachs, H. & Takabatake, Y. (1964). Evidence for a precursor in vasopressin biosynthesis. *Endocrinology* **75**, 943–948.

57. Steiner, D. F., Cunningham, D., Spigelman, L. & Aten, B. (1967). Insulin biosynthesis: evidence for a precursor. *Science* **157**, 697–700.

58. Steiner, D. F., Clark, J. L., Nolan, C., Rubenstein, A. H., Margoliash, E., Aten, B. & Oyer, P. E. (1969). Proinsulin and the biosynthesis of insulin. *Rec. Progr. Horm. Res.* **25**, 207–282.

59. Sachs, H., Fawcett, C. P., Takabatake, Y. & Portanova, R. (1969). Biosynthesis and release of vasopressin and neurophysin. *Rec. Prog. Hormone Res.* **25**, 447–491.

60. Steiner, D. F. (1976). Peptide hormone precursors: biosynthesis, processing and significance. In *Peptide Hormones*. Biological Council—The Co-ordinating

Committee for Symposia on Drug Action (Parsons, J. A., ed.). MacMillan Press, London, pp. 49–65.

61. Blobel, G. & Dobberstein, B. (1975). Transfer of proteins across membranes. I. Presence of proteolytically processed and unprocessed nascent immunoglobulin light chains on membrane-bound ribosomes of murine myeloma. *J. Cell Biol.* **67**, 835–851.

62. Campbell, P. N. & Blobel, G. (1976). The role of organelles in the chemical modification of the primary translation products of secretory proteins. *FEBS Lett.* **72**, 215–226.

63. Jones, C. W. & Pickering, B. T. (1970). Rapid transport of neurohypophysial hormones in the hypothalamoneurohypophysial tract. *J. Physiol. (London)* **208**, 73–74P.

64. Jones, C. W. & Pickering, B. T. (1972). Intra-axonal transport and turnover of neurohypophysial hormones in the rat. *J. Physiol. (London)* **227**, 553–564.

65. Norström, A. & Sjöstrand, J. (1971). Transport and turnover of neurohypophysial proteins of the rat. *J. Neurochem.* **18**, 2007–2016.

66. Burford, G. D. & Pickering, B. T. (1973). Intra-axonal transport and turnover of neurophysins in the rat. A proposal for a possible origin of the minor neurophysin component. *Biochem. J.* **136**, 1047–1052.

67. Sachs, H. (1971). Secretion of neurohypophysial hormones. *Mem. Soc. Endocr.* **19**, 965–973.

68. Gainer, H., Sarne, Y. and Brownstein, M. J. (1977). Neurophysin biosynthesis: Conversion of a putative precursor during axonal transport. *Science* **195**, 1354–1356.

69. Gainer, H., Sarne, Y. & Brownstein, M. J. (1977). Biosynthesis and axonal transport of rat neurohypophysial proteins and peptides. *J. Cell Biol.* **73**, 366–381.

70. Brownstein, M. J., Robinson, A. G. & Gainer, H. (1977). Immunological identification of rat neurophysin precursors. *Nature (London)* **269**, 259–261.

71. Gainer, H. & Brownstein, M. J. (1978). Identification of the precursors of rat neurophysins. In *La Biologie Cellulaire des Processus Neurosecretoires Hypothalamiques* (Vincent, J. D., ed.) (in press).

72. North, W. G., Valkin, H., Morris, J. F. & La Rochelle, F. T. (1977). Evidence for metabolic conversions of rat neurophysins with neurosecretory granules of the hypothamo-neurohypophysial system. *Endocrinology* **101**, 110–118.

73. Pickering, B. T. & Jones, C. W. (1978). The Neurophysins. In *Hormonal Proteins and Peptides*, Vol. 5 (Li, C. H., ed.). Academic Press, New York and London, pp. 103–158.

74. Wuu, T. C. & Crumm, S. E. (1976). Characterization of porcine Neurophysin III: Its resemblance and possible relationship to porcine Neurophysin I. *J. Biol. Chem.* **251**, 2735–2739.

75. Dax, E. M. (1977). Neurophysins and the neurohypophyseal system. Ph.D. thesis. Monash University, Australia.

76. Vogt, M. (1953). Vasopressor, antidiuretic, and oxytocic activities of extracts of the dog's hypothalamus. *Br. J. Pharmacol.* **8**, 193–196.

77. Sachs, H. (1963). Vasopressin Biosynthesis—II. Incorporation of ^{35}S cysteine into vasopressin and protein associated with cell fractions. *J. Neurochem.* **10**, 299–311.

78. Pickering, B. T. (1978). Neurohypophysial hormones—comparative aspects. In *Endocrine Hypothalamus.* (Jeffcoate, S. L. & Hutchinson, J. S. M., ed.). Academic Press, New York and London, pp. 213–227.

79. Hope, D. B. & Pickup, J. C. (1974). Neurophysins. In *The Pituitary Gland and its Neuroendocrine Control*, Handbook of Physiology, Sect. 7, Vol. IV. (Knobil, E. & Sawyer, W. H., eds). American Physiological Society, Washington, D.C., pp. 173–189.

80. Bradbury, A. F., Smyth, D. G. & Snell, C. R. (1976). Prohormones of β-melanotropin (β-melanocyte—stimulating hormone, β-MSH) and corticotropin (adrenocorticotropic hormone, ACTH): structure and activation. In *Polypeptide Hormones: Molecular and Cellular Aspects*, Ciba Foundation Symposium 41 (new series). Excerpta Medica, Amsterdam, pp. 61–75.

81. Pickering, B. T. & McPherson, M. A. (1977). Progress in the study of biosynthesis and transport the neurohypophysial system. In *The Neurohypophysis* (Moses, A. M. & Share, L., eds). Karger, Basle, pp. 30–42.

82. Reichlin, S. & Mitnick, M. A. (1973). Biosynthesis of hypothalamic hypophysiotropic hormones. In *Frontiers in Neuroendocrinology* (Ganong, W. F. & Martini, L., eds). Oxford University Press, Oxford, pp. 61–88.

83. Barnea, A., Ben-Jonathon, N. & Porter, J. C. (1976). Characterization of hypothalamic subcellular particles containing luteinizing hormone-releasing hormone and thyrotropin releasing hormone. *J. Neurochem.* **27**, 477–484.

84. Ishii, S. (1970). Association of luteinizing hormone-releasing factor with granules separated from equine hypophysial stalk. *Endocrinology* **86**, 207–216.

85. McKelvy, J. F. (1977). Biosynthesis of hypothalamic peptides. In *Hypothalamic Peptide Hormones and Pituitary Regulation*. (Porter, J. C., ed.). Plenum Press, New York and London, pp. 77–98.

86. McKelvy, J. F. & Epelbaum, J. (1978). Biosynthesis, packaging, transport and release of brain peptides. In *The Hypothalamus* (Reichlin, S., Baldessarini, R. J. & Martin, J. B., eds). Raven Press, New York.

87. Palkovitz, M. (1977). Biochemical neuroanatomy. In *Endocrinology*, Vol. I (James, V. H. T., ed.). Excerpta Medica, Amsterdam, pp. 105–110.

88. Hughes, J., Smith, T. W., Kosterlitz, H. W., Fothergill, L. A., Morgan, B. A. & Morris, H. R. (1975). Identification of two related pentapeptides from the brain with potent opiate agonist activity. *Nature (London)* **258**, 577–579.

89. Guillemin, R., Ling, N. & Burgus, R. (1976). Endorphines, peptides d'origine hypothalamique et neurohypophysaire avec activité morphinomimetique. *C.R. Hebd. Séances Acad. Sci. Serv. D.* **282**, 783–785.

90. Mains, R. E., Eipper, B. A. & Ling, N. (1977). Common precursor to corticotropins and endorphins. *Proc. Natl. Acad. Sci. U.S.* **74**, 3014–3018.

91. Gainer, H., Loh, Y. P. & Sarne, Y. (1977). Biosynthesis of neuronal peptides. In *Peptides in Neurobiology* (Gainer, H., ed.). Plenum Press, New York, pp. 183–219.

92. Dahlström, A. & Häggendal, J. (1966). Studies on the transport and life span of amine storage granules in a peripheral adrenergic neurone system. *Acta Physiol. Scand.* **67**, 278–288.

93. Dahlström, A. & Häggendal, J. (1967). Studies on the transport and life span of amine storage granules in the adrenergic neurone system of the rabbit sciatic nerve. *Acta Physiol. Scand.* **69**, 153–157.

94. Dahlström, A., Häggendal, J., Heilbronn, E., Heiwall, P-O. & Saunders, N. R. (1974). Proximodistal transport of acetylcholine in peripheral cholinergic neurons. In *Dynamics of Degeneration and Growth in Neurons* (Fuxe, K., Olson, L. and Zotterman, Y., eds). Pergamon Press, Oxford, pp. 275–289.

95. Dalhström, A. (1968). Effect of colchicine on transport of amine storage granules in sympathetic nerves of rat. *Eur. J. Pharmacol.* **5**, 111–113.

96. Malawista, S. E. (1965). On the action of colchicine. The melanocyte model. *J. Exp. Med.* **122**, 361–384.

97. Schmitt, F. O. (1968). Fibrous proteins—neuronal organelles. *Proc. Natn. Acad. Sci. U.S.* **60**, 1092–1101.

98. Schmitt, F. O. (1969). Fibrous proteins and neuronal dynamics. In *Cellular Dynamics of the Neuron* (Barondes, S. H., ed.). Academic Press, New York and London.

99. Huxley, H. E. & Hanson, J. (1954). Changes in cross-striations of muscle during contraction and stretch and their structural interpretation. *Nature (London)* **173**, 973–976.

100. Poisner, A. M. & Douglas, W. W. (1968). A possible mechanism of release of posterior pituitary hormones involving adenosine triphosphate and an adenosine triphosphatase in the neurosecretory granules. *Mol. Pharmacol.* **4**, 531–540.

101. Vilhardt, H. & Hope, D. B. (1974). Adenosine triphosphatase activity in the neural lobe of the bovine pituitary gland. *Biochem. J.* **143**, 181–190.

102. Flament-Durand, J. & Dustin, P. (1972). Studies in the transport of secretory granules in the magnocellular hypothalamic neurons. I. Action of colchicine on axonal flow and neurotubules in the paraventricular nuclei. *Z. Zellforsch Mikrosk. Anat.* **130**, 440–454.

103. Norström, A., Hansson, H. A. & Sjöstrand, J. (1971). Effects of colchicine on axonal transport and ultrastructure of the hypothalamo-neurohypophysial system of the rat. *Z. Zellforsch. Mikrosk. Anat.* **113**, 271–293.

104. Pickering, B. T. (1978). Neurophysins as tools for the study of hypothalamo-neurohypophysial neurones. In *La Biologie Cellulaire des Processus Neurosecretoires Hypothalamiques* (Vincent, J. D., ed.) (in press).

105. Grainger, F. & Sloper, J. C. (1974). Correlation between microtubular number and transport activity of hypothalamoneurohypophyseal secretory neurones. *Cell. Tiss. Res.* **153**, 101–113.

106. Nordmann, J. J. (1977). Ultrastructural morphometry of the rat neurohypophysis. *J. Anat.* **123**, 213–218.

107. Herring, P. T. (1908). The histological appearance of the mammalian pituitary body. *Quart. J. Exp. Physiol.* **1**, 121–159.

108. Douglas, W. W. (1973). "How do neurons secrete peptides?" Exocytosis and its consequences including "synaptic vesicle" formation, in the hypothalamo neurohypophysial system. *Progr. Brain Res.* **39**, 21–39.

109. Douglas, W. W. (1974). Exocytosis and the exocytosis-vesiculation sequence with special reference to neurohypophysis, chromaffin and mast cells, calcium and calcium ionophores. In *Secretory Mechanisms of Exocrine Glands* (Thorn, N. A. & Petersen, O. H. eds). Munksgaard, Copenhagen, Denmark, pp. 801–814.

110. Dreifuss, J. J. (1973). Mécanismes de sécrétion des hormones neurohypophysaires. Aspects cellulaires et sub-cellulaires. *J. Physiol. (Paris)* **67**, 5–52A.

111. Dreifuss, J. J. (1975). A review on neurosecretory granules: their contents and mechanisms of release. *Ann. N.Y. Acad. Sci.* **248**, 184–207.

112. Nordmann, J. J., Dreifuss, J. J. & Legros, J. J. (1971). A correlation of release of polypeptide hormones and of immuno-reactive neurophysin from isolated rat neurohypophyses. *Experientia* **27**, 1344–1345.

113. Matthews, E. K., Legros, J. J., Grau, J. D., Nordmann, J. J. & Dreifuss, J. J. (1973). Release of neurohypophysial hormones by exocytosis. *Nature New Biol.* **241**, 86–88.

114. Edwards, B. A., Edwards, M. E. & Thorn, N. A. (1973). The release *in vitro* of vasopressin unaccompanied by the axoplasmic enzymes: lactic acid dehydrogenase and adenylate kinase. *Acta Endocr. (Copenh.)* **72**, 417–424.

115. Nagasawa, J., Douglas, W. W. & Schulz, R. (1971). Micropinocytotic origin of coated and smooth microvesicles ("synaptic vesicles") in neurosecretory terminals of posterior pituitary glands demonstrated by incorporation of horseradish peroxidase. *Nature (London)* **232**, 341–342.

116. Theodosis, D. T. & Dreifuss, J. J. (1977). Ultrastructural evidence for exoendocytosis in the neurohypophysis. In *Neurohypophysis* (Moses, A. M. & Share, L., eds). Karger, Basle, pp. 88–94.

117. Morris, J. F. (1976). Hormone storage in individual neurosecretory granules of the pituitary gland: a quantitative ultrastructural approach to hormone storage in the neural lobe. *J. Endocr.* **68**, 209–224.

118. Norman, T. C. (1969). Experimentally induced exocytosis of neurosecretory granules. *Exp. Cell Res.* **55**, 285–287.

119. Douglas, W. W., Nagasawa, J. & Schulz, R. (1971). Coated microvesicles in neurosecretory terminals of posterior pituitary glands shed their coats to become smooth "synaptic" vesicles. *Nature (London)* **232**, 340–341.

120. Santolaya, R. C., Bridges, T. E. & Lederis, K. (1972). Elementary granules, small vesicles and exocytosis in the neurohypophysis after acute haemorrhage. *Z. Zellforsch. Mikrosk. Anat.* **125**, 277–288.

121. Nordmann, J. J. & Morris, J. F. (1976). Membrane retrieval at neurosecretory axon endings. *Nature (London)* **261**, 723–725.

122. Nordmann, J. J., Dreifuss, J. J. & Legros, J. J. (1971). A correlation of release of polypeptide hormones and of immunoreactive neurophysin from isolated rat neurohypophyses. *Experientia* **27**, 1344–1345.

123. Castel, M. (1974). *In vitro* uptake of tracers by neurosecretory axon terminals in normal and dehydrated mice. *Gen. Comp. Endocr.* **22**, 336–337.

124. Douglas, W. W. & Rubin, R. P. (1961). The role of calcium in the secretory response of the adrenal medulla to acetylcholine. *J. Physiol. (London)* **159**, 40–57.

125. Douglas, W. W. & Poisner, A. M. (1964). Stimulus secretion coupling in a neurosecretory organ: the role of calcium in the release of vasopressin from the neurohypophysis. *J. Physiol. (London)* **172**, 1–18.

126. Thorn, N. A. (1974). Role of calcium in secretory processes. In *Secretory Mechanisms in Exocrine Glands* (Thorn, N. A. & Petersen, O. H., eds). Munksgaard, Copenhagen, pp. 305–330.

127. Douglas, W. W. (1974). Involvement of calcium in exocytosis and the Exocytosis-Vesiculation sequence. *Biochem. Soc. Symp.* **39**, 1–28.

128. Rubin, R. P. (1970). The role of calcium in the release of neurotransmitter substances and hormones. *Pharmacol. Rev.* **22**, 389–428.

129. Wong, T. M. & Pickering, B. T. (1976). Last in—First out in the neurohypophysis. *Gen. Comp. Endocr.* **29**, 242–243.

130. Norström, A. (1974). The heterogeneity of the neurohypophysial pool of neurophysin. In *Neurosecretion: The Final Neuroendocrine Pathway* (Knowles, F. G. W. & Vollrath, L., eds). Springer, Berlin, pp. 86–93.

131. Sachs, H., Share, L., Osinchak, J. & Carpi, A. (1967). Capacity of the neuro-hypophysis to release vasopressin. *Endocrinology* **81**, 755–770.

132. Thorn, N. A. (1966). *In vitro* studies of the release mechanism for vasopressin in rats. *Acta Endocr. (Copenh.)* **53**, 644–654.

133. Thorn, N. A., Russell, J. T. & Vilhardt, H. (1975). Hexosamine, calcium and neurophysin in secretory granules and the role of calcium in hormone release. *Ann. N.Y. Acad. Sci.* **248**, 202–217.

134. Nordmann, J. J. (1976). Evidence for calcium inactivation during hormone release in the rat neurohypophysis. *J. Exp. Biol.* **65**, 669–683.

135. Howell, S. L. & Lacy, P. E. (1971). Biochemical and ultrastructural studies of insulin storage granules and their secretion. *Membr. Soc. Endocr.* **19**, 469–480.

136. Kopin, I. J., Breese, G. R., Krauss, K. R. & Weise, V. K. (1968). Selective release of newly synthesized norepinephrine from the cat spleen during sympathetic nerve stimulation. *J. Pharmacol. Exp. Ther.* **161**, 271–278.

137. Collier, B. (1969). The preferential release of newly synthesized transmitter by a sympathetic ganglion. *J. Physiol. (London)* **205**, 341–352.

138. Sachs, H. & Haller, E. W. (1968). Further studies on the capacity of the neurohypophysis to release vasopressin. *Endocrinology* **83**, 251–262.

139. Heap, P. F., Jones, C. W., Morris, J. F. & Pickering, B. T. (1975). Movement of neurosecretory product through the anatomical compartments of the neural lobe of the pituitary gland. *Cell Tiss. Res.* **156**, 483–497.

140. Morris, J. F. (1976). Distribution of neurosecretory granules among the anatomical compartments of the neurosecretory processes of the pituitary gland: a quantitative ultrastructural approach to hormone storage in the neural lobe. *J. Endocr.* **68**, 225–234.

141. Jones, C. W. & Pickering, B. T. (1969). Comparison of the effects of water deprivation and sodium chloride imbibition on the hormone content of the neuro-hypophysis of the rat. *J. Physiol. (London)* **203**, 449–458.

142. Pearson, D., Shainberg, A., Osinchak, J. & Sachs, H. (1975). The hypothalamo-neurohypophysial complex in organ culture: morphologic and biochemical characteristics. *Endocrinology* **96**, 982–993.

143. Sladek, C. D. & Knigge, K. M. (1977). Cholinergic stimulation of vasopressin release from the rat hypothalamo-neurohypophyseal system in organ culture. *Endocrinology* **101**, 411–420.

The Control of the Metabolism and the Hormonal Role of Adenosine

J. R. S. ARCH and E. A. NEWSHOLME

Beecham Pharmaceutical Research Division, Nutritional Research Centre, Walton Oaks, Dorking Road, Tadworth, Surrey KT20 7NT, England and Department of Biochemistry, University of Oxford, South Parks Road, Oxford OX1 3QU, England

I. Introduction to Adenosine Metabolism

A. HISTORICAL INTRODUCTION

Reis discovered in the 1930s that adenosine is produced by the hydrolysis of 5'-AMP[1] and deduced that the reaction was catalysed by an enzyme specific for 5'-nucleotides, now known as 5'-nucleotidase (EC 3.1.3.5). Since it was already known that adenosine could be converted to inosine by adenosine deaminase[2] (EC 3.5.4.4), the nucleotide could be assigned as an intermediate in adenine nucleotide degradation. It was assumed that adenine nucleotide biosynthesis occurred via a reverse of the degradative reactions and this view was supported when, in the early 1950s, it was found that rat tissues incorporate labelled adenosine into adenine nucleotides and RNA.[3] Furthermore, the enzyme adenosine kinase, which could initiate this incorporation, was discovered in 1951.[4,5] However, it was soon demonstrated that the pathway for adenine nucleotide formation from small molecules (i.e. *de novo* synthesis) did not involve adenosine: it involved a cyclic ribonucleotide, so that adenine and adenosine were bypassed by this biosynthetic process.[6] At this stage, the physiological significance of the ability of rat tissues to incorporate adenosine into adenine nucleotides and RNA was unknown.

In 1957 it was proposed that adenosine kinase is a component of a "salvage pathway" which reduces the loss of the purine; thus adenosine, produced from nucleic acid degradation, could be re-converted to adenine nucleotides by the enzyme.[7] Although this could explain the role of adenosine kinase, it posed a problem of the role of the 5'-nucleotidase reaction. Why is adenosine produced from AMP only to be converted back to AMP? The hypothesis presented in this Essay is that adenosine is produced because it is a local hormone (i.e. similar to prostaglandins, its effects are mainly localized to the organ in which it is produced). As such its steady-state concentration is controlled via specific adenosine-forming and utilizing reactions. The properties of these reactions will be reviewed in some detail in this Essay, since they provide the basis for the theories of control of the concentration of this local messenger molecule. Although the biochemical mechanisms of control in different tissues may be similar, the biochemical and physiological effects of adenosine are very diverse, and it is studied by workers in very different fields (e.g. regulation of blood flow, lipolysis, neurotransmission, smooth muscle physiology, platelet aggregation). Consequently, we are reviewing the biochemistry of the mechanisms that control changes in adenosine concentration in order to provide a common basis on which to consider the relationship between the biochemistry, physiology and pharmacology of adenosine.

B. PATHWAYS OF ADENOSINE METABOLISM

Adenosine is produced, released, taken up and metabolized by most animal tissues. The concentrations of adenosine under physiological conditions range from about $1\cdot0$ to 30 nmol g^{-1} wet wt. and $<0\cdot03$ to $2\cdot6$ μM for tissues and body fluids respectively (see Tables 1 and 2). A number of pathways could be involved in adenosine metabolism (see Fig. 1). However, some of these pathways are of little or no quantitative significance, at least in tissues discussed in this Essay.

Acid or alkaline phosphatases (EC 3.1.3.2 and 3.1.3.1) could be involved in the formation of adenosine since they catalyse the hydrolysis of 5'-AMP to adenosine. However, they show no specificity for 5'-AMP and their activities at neutral pH are too low to be of quantitative physiological importance in

TABLE 1

Adenosine content of mammalian tissues

Animals	Tissue	Treatment of tissue	Adenosine content (nmol g^{-1} fresh wt.)
Rat[8]	Heart	Control	$2\cdot4$
		5 s ischaemia	$4\cdot9$
		25 s ischaemia	$18\cdot0$
Dog[10]	Calf muscle	Control	$2\cdot0$
		10 min stimulation	$8\cdot4$
Rat[11]	Brain	Control	$4\cdot3$
		5 min stimulation	$10\cdot5$
		Arterial blood pressure reduced from 85 to 45 mm Hg	$17\cdot5$
		Oxygen content of inspired air reduced from 21 to 11%	30
Dog[12]	Cerebral cortex	Control	$11\cdot4$
		1 min ischaemia	$28\cdot2$
Guinea-pig[13]	Brain neocortex	Control	$2\cdot25$
		Control Brain neocortex slices	$1\cdot97$
		2 min hypoxia	$16\cdot25$
		10 min stimulation	$5\cdot24$
		Noradrenaline ($0\cdot1$ mM)	$5\cdot15$
		Histamine ($0\cdot1$ mM)	$2\cdot20$
		Glutamate (4 mM)	$15\cdot22$
		Glutamate and stimulation	$33\cdot89$
Dog[14]	Lung	Control	$0\cdot56$
		Ventilated with 95% N_2, 5% CO_2 for 3 min	$4\cdot9$

TABLE 2

Concentration of adenosine in body fluids and tissue perfusates

Animal	Treatment of animal or tissue		Concentration of adenosine (μM)
Rat[15]	Coronary perfusate	Control	<0·1
		9·5 min anoxia	1·3
Cat[16]	Coronary perfusate	Control	0·015
		Anoxic	0·15
		Adrenaline (0·3 μg^{-1} ml)	2·6
Dog[17]	Coronary sinus blood	Control	<0·03
		After 30–60 s ischaemia	0·13
Dog[18]	Pericardial fluid	Control	1·09
Rat[19]	Hind limb perfusate	Control	<0·03
		12 min after stimulation for 3 min	0·28
Dog[10]	Venous blood from calf muscle	Control	0·11
		2 min stimulation	0·16
Dog[20]	Hind limb venous plasma	Control	0·7
		After ischaemia and stimulation for 5 min	1·5
Dog[12]	Cerebrospinal fluid	Control	0·22
		After 6 min ischaemia	0·89
Man[21]	Blood plasma	Control	0·31
		Adenosine deaminase deficient boy	1·4

adenosine production.[22, 23] Similarly, purine nucleotide phosphorylase (EC 2.4.2.1), which could produce adenosine from adenine, has a very low activity.[24] On the other hand, 5′-nucleotidase is specific for 5′-nucleotides,[1, 25] its pH optimum is close to the physiological pH and its maximal activity can more than adequately account for known rates of adenosine formation.[26]

Adenosine is converted, either *in vivo* or *in vitro*, to inosine or adenine nucleotides. The enzymes, adenosine deaminase and adenosine kinase, are considered to be responsible for these conversions. However, although the involvement of adenosine deaminase in the formation of inosine has never been questioned, it has been suggested that adenosine kinase is not involved in the formation of adenine nucleotides.[27–29] Two other pathways have been put forward. First, the phosphorolysis of adenosine to adenine, catalysed by purine nucleoside phosphorylase, followed by reaction of adenine with 5-phosphoribosyl-1-pyrophosphate to form AMP (see Fig. 1). This pathway is unlikely to be of quantitative importance since the activity of the phosphorylase is very low.[24] Moreover, when adenosine, is labelled with ^{14}C in the purine

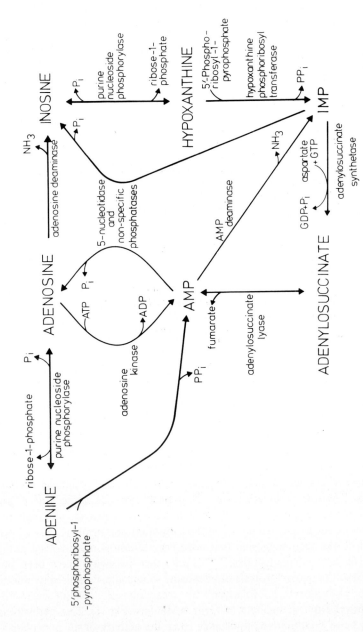

Fig 1. Possible pathways of adenosine metabolism. The inclusion of a pathway in this figure does not necessarily signify that it is important in animal tissues.

ring, is incorporated into adenine nucleotides by intact tissues or homogenates, none of the label is incoporated into adenine.[3,26,30,31] The second suggested pathway is the conversion of inosine to hypoxanthine and then to IMP (see Fig. 1). However, various lines of evidence suggest that this pathway is quantitatively unimportant and that the adenosine kinase reaction is important for the conversion of adenosine into adenine nucleotides. First, the maximum activities of adenosine kinase are similar to or greater than the rates of conversion of adenosine to adenine nucleotides.[26,32] Secondly, the rate of incorporation of [14C]adenosine into adenine nucleotides by human erythrocytes or homogenates of pig heart is not decreased by addition of unlabelled hypoxanthine or inosine.[30,33] Thirdly, the ratio of the radioactivity in the purine and ribose moieties of [14C]adenosine is not changed when adenosine is incorporated into adenine nucleotides by intact tissues,[34,35] whereas the rate of incorporation of the purine moiety of inosine into adenine nucleotides is considerably greater than that of the ribose moiety;[36] this indicates that

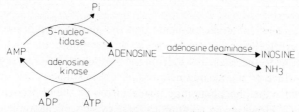

Fig. 2. Enzymes involved in adenosine metabolism.

adenosine is not converted to inosine prior to formation of the nucleotide. Finally, cell-free systems (i.e. haemolysates of human erythrocytes) incorporate the γ-phosphate group of [γ-32P] ATP into AMP in the presence of adenosine;[37] the only reasonable mechanism for this reaction is direct phosphorylation of adenosine by adenosine kinase.

We conclude, therefore, that adenosine is produced from AMP by 5'-nucleotidase and, it is either reconverted to AMP by adenosine kinase or deaminated to inosine by adenosine deaminase (Fig. 2).

Detailed discussion of the mechanisms whereby these three enzymes control the concentration of adenosine is deferred (Section IV) until its release from and uptake into the cell has been reviewed. This is essential before we can consider the control of the adenosine concentration.

II. Release of Adenosine from the Cell

For adenosine to serve as a local hormone (i.e. an informational link between different tissues or cells within one organ), it must be released from the cell. The simplest hypothesis for the biochemical mechanism of release is that adenosine is produced intracellularly and is then transported across the cell membrane by a carrier-mediated process (facilitated diffusion) according to its concentration gradient. However, the major problem with this hypothesis is the localization of 5'-nucleotidase: there is considerable evidence that, in some tissues, this enzyme is localized on the plasma membrane and that it can hydrolyse extracellular AMP (i.e. it can be described as an ectoenzyme). Consequently, adenosine may be produced directly into the extracellular space.

A. LOCALIZATION OF 5'-NUCLEOTIDASE

Cell fractionation and cytochemical studies have shown that, in many tissues (e.g. brain,[38] liver,[39] lung,[40] heart and skeletal muscle[9]) a large proportion of the 5'-nucleotidase activity is associated with the plasma membrane: indeed this activity is frequently used as a marker for the plasma membrane of liver cells.[39] Histochemical, developmental and clinical studies suggest that some of the enzyme is associated with the myelin sheath in brain.[41,42]

Some cytochemical studies indicate that the plasma membrane enzyme has access to extracellular substrate, since a precipitate of lead or osmium phosphate (due to the release of P_i from the 5'-nucleotidase reaction) is seen on the outer surface of the plasma membrane. These studies must be interpreted cautiously since the phosphate may migrate from its site of production prior to precipitation.[43] However, in addition to these cytochemical studies, kinetic and immunological[44,45] studies suggest that the plasma membrane enzyme is an ectoenzyme. Thus externally added AMP is rapidly hydrolysed by intact cells (brain slices,[46] liver cells,[47] perfused liver,[15,48] skeletal muscle,[15,49] fat cells,[45] adipose tissue,[48] lung[40]). Hydrolysis occurs without significant penetration of AMP through the plasma membrane and disruption of the cells does not increase the rate of hydrolysis.[15,45,47] Externally added ATP[46] and cyclic AMP[48] are likewise rapidly metabolized to adenosine by intact cells, so that some ATPase and cyclic AMP phosphodiesterase activity must also be on the outer surface of the cell.

Despite this evidence, other cytochemical and fractionation studies of brain,[49] liver,[25,42,43] heart and skeletal muscle,[52,9] show that much of the nucleotidase activity is not associated with the plasma membrane but with other organelles or the cytosol. Thus a high proportion (40–80%) of nucleotidase activity is present in the soluble fraction of avian heart and pectoral muscle.[53]

The cellular localization of 5'-nucleotidase activity in mammalian heart and skeletal muscle is unclear. It may be exclusively in vascular cells[54,55] but there is good evidence for an additional association with the membranes of muscle cells.[9] A further opinion is that, in mammalian heart, adenosine is produced entirely in perivascular mesenchymal cells, which are situated between the myocardial cells and the coronary arterioles.[56]

B. HYPOTHESES FOR THE ROLE OF MEMBRANE-BOUND 5'-NUCLEOTIDASE IN CONTROL OF ADENOSINE RELEASE

There is little doubt that in many tissues a considerable proportion of the nucleotidase has access to extracellular AMP as substrate, but it is not clear if the enzyme has access to only extracellular or to both intra- and extracellular AMP. These two possibilities are discussed below.

(1) Extracellular AMP as substrate for 5'-nucleotidase

This hypothesis proposes that nucleotidase hydrolyses exclusively extracellular AMP, which is derived from either extracellular ATP or cyclic AMP. The source of the extracellular ATP and/or cyclic AMP is intracellular. Thus there is evidence that ATP is released from nerve endings (either alone or in association with catecholamine or acetylcholine release[57]) and that cyclic AMP is released from a number of tissues.[58–60] The extracellular ATP and cyclic AMP can be degraded to AMP by ectoenzymes.[47,48,61–63] Indeed many effects ascribed to exogenous cyclic AMP may be due to adenosine, since the nucleoside is often more potent than the cyclic nucleotide[64] (see Section VI.D). This conversion could also explain the observation that exogenous cyclic AMP sometimes produces a very different effect from its more lipid soluble analogue, dibutyryl cyclic AMP.[64–66] The latter is probably not metabolized by the external phosphodiesterase so that it enters the cell unchanged. The isoprenaline-stimulated rate of release of cyclic AMP from perfused rat heart is 0.5 nmol min^{-1} g^{-1} fresh tissue.[59] This rate is insufficient to account for maximal rates of adenosine formation in heart but it could make a significant contribution to the basal rate (Table 6). Unfortunately, reliable values for rates of release of ATP have not been obtained owing to its rapid hydrolysis in blood and the problem of ATP release from damaged blood cells.[19]

(2) Intra- and extracellular AMP as substrates for 5'-nucleotidase

This hypothesis proposes that the membrane-bound 5'-nucleotidase can hydrolyse both intra- and extracellular AMP, but that under normal conditions the enzyme utilizes primarily intracellular AMP. The hypothesis permits the enzyme to be regulated by changes in the intracellular concentration of AMP and other metabolites (see Section IV). Furthermore, the adenosine is released directly into the extracellular space, so that the enzyme functions both as a nucleotidase and as a transport system.

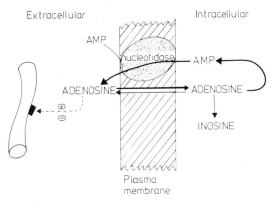

Fig. 3. Plasma membrane localization of 5'-nucleotidase in relation to control of adenosine concentration. The broader lines indicate the major direction of adenosine metabolism in the basal condition.

Unfortunately, the available evidence does not differentiate between these two hypotheses. We prefer hypothesis (2) for those tissues, such as muscle, in which the rate of adenosine production increases when the intracellular concentration of AMP increases. Nevertheless, hypothesis (1) probably accounts for a proportion of the adenosine production in some organs.

Although there is doubt about the precise localization of adenosine production, most of the utilization of adenosine occurs intracellularly. If adenosine is produced (or released) on the external surface of the cell and utilization occurs within the cell, the direction of transport of adenosine will be into the cell (see Fig. 3).

III. Uptake of Adenosine by the Cell

The release of adenosine is only one of the processes that regulates the concentration of extracellular adenosine (i.e. the concentration of the local hormone at its site of action). The second process that is essential for the maintenance of the steady-state concentration of adenosine is its removal from the extracellular space. The rate of removal may also play a role in changing the concentration of adenosine from one steady-state to another.

The mechanism that is quantitatively most important in the removal of adenosine is uptake into cells in the vicinity of its site of action followed by intracellular metabolism. Very little adenosine escapes from the organ, in which it is produced into the general circulation. Thus the concentration of adenosine in blood and other body fluids is much lower than that in the tissues[15] (see Tables 1 and 2), even though a significant proportion of tissue adenosine may be in the extracellular space (see also Section IV.C). The small proportion of adenosine that enters the general circulation is probably either metabolized by extracellular adenosine deaminase (see below) or is removed by the blood cells, lung, spleen or liver.[26,68,69]

It seems unlikely that the extracellular metabolism of adenosine by adenosine kinase or adenosine deaminase is quantitatively important. There is evidence that some deaminase is extracellular in neuroblastoma and astrocyte cultures[47] and rat heart[61] but most deaminase activity is cytosolic.[49,52,71] Even if a proportion of adenosine deaminase is extracellular, it probably plays a very minor quantitative role compared with phosphorylation in adenosine metabolism (see Section IV).

A. BIOCHEMISTRY OF ADENOSINE UPTAKE

The uptake of adenosine by tissues involves two processes: transport across the plasma membrane and metabolism within the cell (Fig. 4). These two processes provide a simple metabolic system for the uptake of adenosine and its conversion either to compounds that are transported less rapidly across the cell membrane or to those that are less potent in the extracellular environment.

Adenosine transport across the cell membrane does not appear to be an active process, since the intracellular concentration has never been found to exceed the extracellular concentration.[35,70] It is likely that transport occurs via a carrier-mediated (facilitated diffusion) process, although simple diffusion may play a small role.

Part of the evidence for the carrier-mediated mechanism is that the rate of transport responds in a hyperbolic manner to an increase in adenosine concentration.[35,72-76] In addition, a rise in temperature of 10°C increases the rate of transport by about two-fold,[70,75,77,78] which is a greater effect than would be expected for simple diffusion. However, caution must be used in the

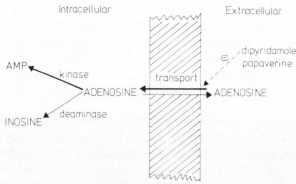

Fig. 4. Processes involved in the uptake of adenosine. The thicker lines indicate the direction of adenosine metabolism in the basal condition.

TABLE 3

K_m values of adenosine kinase and adenosine uptake for adenosine

Animal	Tissue	K_m values (μM)	
		Adenosine uptake	Adenosine kinase
Guinea-pig	Heart	1[72]	—
Rat	Heart	5[17]	0.7[26]
Dog	Heart	11.6[73]	0.4[73]
Guinea-pig	Brain	20[35]	20[35]
Rat	Brain	—	1.5[26]
Rat	Hepatoma cells	10[82]	5.8[87]
Human	Erythrocyte ghosts	7.5[78]	1.9[88]
Dog	Erythrocytes	90[75]	—
Human	Platelets	9.8[78] 9400	—
Pig	Aortic endothelial cells	3[74] 250	—
Mouse	Lymphocytes	12[81] 400	—

interpretation of these experiments since uptake of adenosine rather than transport was measured (the uptake process includes both transport and intracellular metabolism). If intracellular metabolism was rate limiting for uptake of adenosine, both saturation kinetics and a high temperature dependency would be expected since intracellular metabolism is enzymic. Thus some values of K_m for the uptake process may reflect values of K_m for adenosine kinase (see Table 3). It cannot be emphasized too strongly that in order to study the mechanism of transport, the rate of uptake must be limited by transport.

Nevertheless, there is further evidence that implicates a carrier-mediated process. Uptake is inhibited both by other nucleosides (e.g. inosine, uridine, thymidine), which apparently share the same transport mechanism,[77] and by a number of compounds (e.g. dipyridamole, papaverine, hexobendine, p-nitrobenzylthioguanosine, reserpine[77–80]) which do not share the transport mechanism. These compounds have little or no effect on the activities of adenosine kinase or deaminase in cell-free systems so that they presumably reduce uptake by inhibition of transport rather than inhibition of intracellular metabolism.

Simple diffusion of adenosine may play some role in its transport in some tissues. The rate of this component of uptake increases linearly with increasing concentration of adenosine[70,72,82] and is increased at most 1.3-fold by a rise in temperature of 10°C[70,78] However, this component of uptake may in part reflect the activity of adenosine deaminase, which is saturated at considerably higher concentrations of adenosine than the kinase (see Section IV). This suggestion is supported by the finding of a second higher K_m value for uptake in some cells (see Table 3) and by the observation that the Q_{10} value of adenosine deaminase is very low.[26] Moreover, it explains why dipyridamole and papaverine inhibit the non-saturable or high-K_m as well as the low-K_m component of uptake:[70,74] by inhibiting transport, dipyridamole reduces the concentration of adenosine available to both adenosine kinase and adenosine deaminase.

B. LOCALIZATION OF ADENOSINE

The evidence that is available at present suggests that the rate of uptake of adenosine by tissues is primarily regulated by the intracellular activities of adenosine kinase and adenosine deaminase and not by the activity of the transport process. Thus, if labelled adenosine or an analogue of adenosine is injected into an animal, the radioactivity is distributed between the organs roughly in proportion to the activity of adenosine kinase.[26] Inhibitors of adenosine kinase also inhibit adenosine uptake by tissues[35] and, when metabolism is inhibited, inhibitors of transport have little effect on the rate of uptake.[76]

Nonetheless, in some tissues, the activity of the transport mechanism may be sufficiently low, in comparison to the processes metabolizing adenosine, that the concentration of adenosine does not equilibrate across the cell membrane. Consequently, the concentration of adenosine available to the kinase and deaminase is less than the extracellular concentration. Some evidence for this is that cell lysis usually increases the rate of metabolism of exogenous adenosine[73,82] whereas inhibitors of transport inhibit metabolism.[77-80]

The distribution of adenosine between intra- and extracellular spaces must be known in order to understand fully the control of its concentration and more direct and definite studies than those described above are needed. These experiments would be analogous to those carried out on glucose metabolism in heart and diaphragm[84,85] and would employ freeze-clamping the tissue instead of the relatively slow cooling methods used for some studies on adenosine metabolism.[70,80,86]

IV. Metabolic Regulation of Adenosine Concentration

To develop a theory of metabolic control of the concentration of adenosine based on the properties of 5'-nucleotidase, adenosine kinase and adenosine deaminase, it is essential to know whether the enzymes catalyse near- or non-equilibrium reactions.[89] Allosteric regulation can only produce large changes in the flux through the adenosine pathway and hence in the concentration of adenosine if the enzymes catalyse non-equilibrium reactions.[90] (So far in these discussions it has been tacitly assumed that the reactions are non-equilibrium.)

TABLE 4

Equilibrium constants and mass-action ratios for the reactions catalysed by 5′-nucleotidase, adenosine kinase and adenosine deaminase

Enzyme	Ratio studied	$K_{eq.}$	Mass action ratios (Γ)*			
			Rat heart		Rat skeletal muscle	
			Aerobic	Anaerobic	Aerobic	Anaerobic and stimulated
5′-Nucleotidase	$\dfrac{[\text{Adenosine}][\text{Pi}]}{[\text{AMP}]}$	300^{92}	0·0002	0·004	0·0004	0·002
Adenosine kinase	$\dfrac{[\text{AMP}][\text{ADP}]}{[\text{ATP}][\text{Adenosine}]}$	3400^{92}	10	4	2	7
Adenosine deaminase	$\dfrac{[\text{Inosine}][\text{NH}_3]}{[\text{Adenosine}]}$	17000^{93}	0·0007	0·005	0·0007	0·017

* For concentrations of nucleotides and nucleosides see reference 9; for concentrations of Pi and NH_3 see references 94—96.

The best method for deducing the equilibrium nature of a reaction is comparison of the mass-action ratio (Γ) with the equilibrium constant (K_{eq}). If the ratio, K_{eq}/Γ, is large (>5) the reaction is considered to be non-equilibrium whereas if it is close to unity (<5) the reaction is considered to be close to equilibrium.[91] Values of Γ and K_{eq} for the reactions of adenosine metabolism are given in Table 4. From these data it is clear that all three enzymes catalyse non-equilibrium reactions. Therefore the *in vitro* properties of the enzymes may be relevant *in vivo*.

A. PROPERTIES OF THE ENZYMES RELEVANT TO METABOLIC CONTROL

The activity of an enzyme that catalyses a non-equilibrium reaction may be regulated acutely by changes in the concentrations of substrates, co-substrates or allosteric effectors or by changes in the rate of interconversion between different forms of the enzyme (i.e. isoenzymes) with markedly different catalytic activities.[89,97] The activity may be regulated more slowly by changes in the concentration of the enzyme. Little or nothing is known of this slow regulation or of enzymic interconversions of the enzymes of adenosine metabolism, so that only the effects of changes in the concentrations of substrates and allosteric effectors are considered.

(1) 5'-Nucleotidase

K_m values for 5'-nucleotidase range from 4 to 12,000 μM,[15,25,26,98] but it is unlikely that the high values reflect a physiologically important enzyme for the formation of adenosine. Values of between 22 and 123 μM were obtained in one study using crude homogenates of a number of vertebrate tissues[26] (although values were higher for some invertebrate tissues). Since crude homogenates were used in this study, these K_m values are probably those of the enzyme that is quantitatively most important for adenosine production in each tissue *in vivo*.

The activities of 5'-nucleotidase from various vertebrate sources are strongly inhibited by ATP, ADP and their phosphonate analogues[45,99–101] and by other nucleoside triphosphates.[101–102] ATP or ADP inhibits at micromolar concentrations so that, at physiological concentrations of these nucleotides, the enzyme would be almost totally inactive. However, this effect of ATP or ADP is markedly reduced by the presence of equimolar concentrations of Mg^{2+}[53,98,100] (the adipose tissue enzyme may be an exception[25]) and the ATP–Mg and ADP–Mg complexes may not inhibit the enzyme.[53] Since phosphorus NMR studies on living muscle indicate that at least 95% of the ATP in the muscle is complexed with Mg^{2+},[103] the inhibition of the enzyme by ATP and

ADP *in vivo* may be markedly less than predicted from the *in vitro* studies in the absence of Mg^{2+}.

(2) Adenosine deaminase

In general, the K_m values for adenosine deaminase fall within the range 6 to 60 μM.[26, 104, 105] The enzyme is notable in that very few potentially physiological modifiers of its activity have been discovered, despite extensive investigations.

(3) Adenosine kinase

The K_m value of adenosine kinase for adenosine ranges from <0.4 to 5.8 μM for vertebrate tissues (see Table 3), although there is a report of a value of 20 μM for the enzyme from guinea-pig brain.[25] The enzyme from some species is inhibited at pH 7.0–7.5 by concentrations of adenosine that are slightly higher than the K_m value but substrate inhibition has never been found at pH 5.3–5.8.[26, 106]

The activity of adenosine kinase from some mouse, chicken and pigeon tissues is reduced by about 50% when the concentrations of monovalent cations in the assay medium are changed from 140 mM Na^+ to 120 mM Na^+ and 20 mM K^+.[26] The effect results largely from inhibition by K^+, although Na^+ produces slight activation. A similar change in the concentrations of Na^+ and K^+ had little effect on adenosine kinase from frog, locust and earthworm tissues.[26]

B. THEORY FOR THE METABOLIC REGULATION OF ADENOSINE CONCENTRATION

A theory for the control of adenosine concentration can be proposed on the basis of the above properties of 5'-nucleotidase, adenosine deaminase and adenosine kinase. The theory is illustrated in Fig. 5. It applies primarily to those tissues in which 5'-nucleotidase hydrolyses intracellular AMP, but it can be applied with a few modifications to tissues in which 5'-nucleotidase hydrolyses extracellular AMP derived from the degradation of ATP or cyclic AMP (see Section II). The theory assumes that the rate of transport of adenosine across the cell membrane is a near-equilibrium process controlled only by changes in the intra- and extracellular concentrations of adenosine. Since the basis for the theory is that adenosine is produced directly into the extracellular space and is utilized by the intracellular kinase and deaminase, the net direction of adenosine transport must always be inwards (see Fig. 5). Inhibitors of transport should, therefore, raise the extracellular concentration of adenosine and lower that intracellularly.

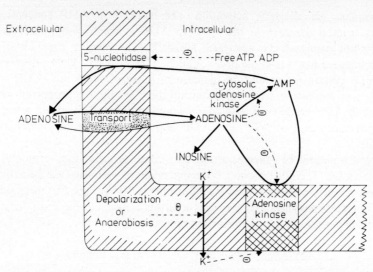

Fig. 5. Hypothesis of the control of concentration of adenosine. Dotted lines indicate regulatory effects: + indicates stimulation; − indicates inhibition.

(1) Control of 5'-nucleotidase activity

At the present time, the precise concentration of AMP that would be available to the nucleotidase is not known. It is likely that some of the measured levels of AMP do not reflect the concentration in the cytosol, since it is probably bound to protein[107] and may also be localized within mitochondria.[108] The free concentration of AMP in the cytosol of heart and liver may be approximately 6 and 20 μM respectively. If it is assumed that this AMP is available to the membrane bound 5'-nucleotidase (see Section II), the substrate concentration will be below the K_m value.

It is well established that increased work (metabolic, biosynthetic, ion pumping, muscle contraction) in a tissue will increase the AMP concentration. Further, even the slightest hypoxia causes an increase in the concentration of AMP in tissues.[109,110] Since the AMP concentration available to 5'-nucleotidase may be well below the K_m of the enzyme for AMP, the increased concentration of AMP would produce a linear increase in the enzyme activity (e.g. a four-fold increase in substrate concentration would produce a four-fold increase in the activity of the enzyme) and hence an increase in the concentration of adenosine. There is no evidence of sigmoidicity in the response of nucleotidase activity to substrate concentration which would produce a larger change in enzyme activity than that indicated above.

It is, however, possible that the changes which cause the increase in AMP concentration in the cell also cause a further increase in the activity of the nucleotidase via allosteric activation. The increase in AMP concentration results from a decrease in the ATP to ADP concentration ratio (via the equilibrium catalysed by adenylate kinase[89]). The binding constant of the nucleotides for Mg^{2+} is in the order ATP > ADP > AMP. Thus a decrease in the ATP concentration and an increase in those of ADP and AMP could produce an increase in free Mg^{2+} concentration, so that the proportion of the ATP and ADP complexed with Mg^{2+} would increase. This would lower the free concentrations of ATP and ADP and hence reduce the inhibition of nucleotidase.

The formation of adenosine is only one process that regulates its concentration. The other process is the utilization of adenosine via the activities of the enzymes, adenosine kinase and deaminase. There are two mechanisms involving these enzymes that may play a further important role in producing or increasing changes in the adenosine concentration.

(2) *Effect of ions on adenosine kinase activity*

In some tissues, a proportion (up to 20%) of the activity of adenosine kinase is associated with cell membranes.[32,70] From the properties of the kinase, it can be proposed that a small increase in the K^+ concentration in the immediate environment of the cell membrane could inhibit the kinase activity. Such changes in the K^+ concentration would be produced by membrane depolarization or hypoxia,[10,11] so that the steady-state concentration of adenosine would be increased. Changes in the kinase activity *per se* would produce a change in the steady-state concentration of adenosine. However, it is likely that changes in the K^+ concentration in the vicinity of the cell membrane reflect a physiological condition that will also cause an increase in AMP concentration and a decrease in free ATP and ADP concentrations. Thus the decrease in kinase activity should complement an increase in nucleotidase activity and lead to a larger increase in the extracellular (and intracellular) concentration of adenosine.

(3) *Increased sensitivity due to kinetic properties of adenosine kinase and deaminase*

The activities of 5'-nucleotidase and adenosine kinase produce a substrate cycle between AMP and adenosine, as follows:

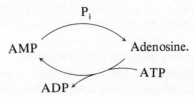

There is considerable evidence that both the hydrolysis of AMP and the phosphorylation of adenosine occur simultaneously—a necessary requirement for a substrate cycle (see p. 101). To understand the significance of this cycle it is important to appreciate that the kinase has a low K_m for adenosine, whereas that for the deaminase is perhaps 50-fold higher.[26] Indeed, the K_m of the kinase is lower than the overall tissue concentration of adenosine under basal conditions (see Tables 1 and 3), but, since the intracellular concentration is somewhat less than the extracellular concentration (see Section III), the K_m of the kinase and the intracellular concentration are probably similar. Therefore, the kinase may approach saturation with substrate, even under basal conditions, whereas the concentration of adenosine is well below the K_m of the deaminase. When the concentration of adenosine is increased (e.g. by an increase in the activity of 5'-nucleotidase) the activity of the kinase will increase very little. Consequently, almost all of the additional adenosine production will be metabolized by adenosine deaminase. However, the only reason why the deaminase activity should increase under these conditions is the increase in adenosine concentration. The increase in the concentration of adenosine must be much greater than the increase in the rate of adenosine production, as the following simple calculation shows:

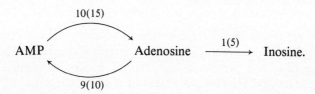

The first set of numbers represent the flux of residues through the reactions in the basal steady-state situation. The numbers in parentheses represent the steady-state fluxes after the nucleotidase activity has increased by 50%. Since adenosine almost saturates the kinase, 80% of the increased flux is metabolized via the deaminase. The only means by which the deaminase can increase its activity from 1 to 5 units is by a five-fold increase (at least) in the concentration of adenosine. In this way, the change in the activity of the nucleotidase is amplified and there is a larger change in the concentration of adenosine. In fact, the amplification may be considerably greater than the calculation above suggests, since adenosine kinase from some species is inhibited by concentrations of adenosine that are only slightly higher than the K_m value. Thus, when the flux through 5'-nucleotidase increases, the flux through adenosine kinase may actually decrease.

The role of substrate cycles in providing increased sensitivity in metabolic control has been discussed in detail elsewhere.[91] The improved sensitivity is proportional to the ratio of the cycling rate to the flux. The same quantitative

TABLE 5

Effect of cycling rate between adenosine and AMP on change in adenosine concentration

$$\text{AMP} \underset{2}{\overset{1}{\rightleftarrows}} \text{Adenosine} \xrightarrow{3} \text{Inosine}$$

Fold-change in nucleotidase activity	Nucleotidase activity (1)	Cycling rate (2)	Flux (3)	Cycling/ flux	Fold-change in adenosine concentration
Basal	11	1	10	0·1	basal
5	55	1	54	—	5·4*
Basal	25	15	10	1·5	basal
5	125	15	110	—	11·0*
Basal	50	40	10	4·0	basal
5	250	40	210	—	21*
Basal	200	190	10	19·0	basal
5	1000	190	810	—	81*

* Assumes that adenosine deaminase responds linearly to an increased concentration of adenosine and that the system is in steady state.

argument applies to the change in adenosine concentration (see Table 5). Under basal conditions, adenosine is mostly rephosphorylated. This preserves the purine base and permits a high rate of cycling in relation to flux of adenosine to inosine. However, in situations of stress, it is advantageous for the cell to permit the degradation of adenosine to inosine so that ATP is not used for the rephosphorylation of adenosine and the ATP to ADP concentration ratio of the cell is maintained. Energy must be used for the resynthesis of AMP from inosine (or smaller molecules) but this may be delayed until the animal has recovered from or adapted to the stress situation.

As a result of the effects of free ATP and ADP concentrations on 5'-nucleotidase activity, inhibition of adenosine kinase by K^+ and the substrate cycle between adenosine and AMP, the change in concentration of adenosine is considerably greater than that of AMP. This would permit rapid diffusion of adenosine both within the extracellular space and from there to the intra-cellular space.

C. EVIDENCE FOR THE THEORY OF METABOLIC REGULATION

The theory of control of adenosine concentration presented above predicts that the activity of 5'-nucleotidase and the tissue concentration of adenosine should increase under conditions that increase the concentration of AMP. Furthermore, the increase in the steady-state concentration of adenosine should be proportionally greater than the increase in AMP concentration.

The available data on changes in the concentration of adenosine under different conditions are consistent with these predictions. For example, hypoxia, which decreases the ATP to ADP concentration ratio in the cell and also increases the extracellular K^+ concentration, produces a 3·8-fold increase in AMP concentration and a 22-fold increase in adenosine concentration in ischaemic rat heart.[9]

Unfortunately, these data do not indicate the extent to which the mechanisms described above (concentrations of AMP, free ATP, K^+; kinetic properties of the kinase and deaminase) contribute to the increase in adenosine concentration. Nor indeed do they indicate whether the change in adenosine concentration is due to a change in the rate of production or utilization of the messenger. It should be possible to test the theory further by measuring the rate of release of adenosine by tissues and rates of phosphorylation and deamination of labelled adenosine. This is discussed below.

(1) The rate of adenosine release

There are a number of problems associated with the measurement of the rate of adenosine release from tissues. First, adenosine may be released from the cell together with other nucleotides (e.g. cyclic AMP, ATP) which are subsequently degraded to adenosine by ectoenzymes. Indeed, it has been shown that electrically-stimulated guinea-pig brain slices release both adenine nucleotides and adenosine. The proportion of adenosine released was estimated as 70%.[112] Secondly, adenosine may be degraded to inosine and hypoxanthine, so that the release of all three compounds should be measured. Thirdly, it is important to realize that most of the adenosine that is released will be taken up again, whereas it is the overall release that is required as a measure of the activity of 5'-nucleotidase. This problem could be circumvented by measuring release in the presence of an inhibitor of adenosine uptake. Alternatively, release and uptake can be calculated from simultaneous measurements of both the uptake of labelled adenosine and the release of unlabelled adenosine.[34] Finally, the adenine nucleotides of the tissue can be prelabelled using [^{14}C]adenine and release of labelled adenosine into a large pool of unlabelled adenosine can be followed. (Some workers have apparently used this approach unwittingly:[112,113] their data suggest that 75–80% of the adenosine released from guinea-pig brain slices and rabbit heart is taken up again.)

As a result of these problems, there are no precise estimates of 5'-nucleotidase activity *in vivo*. Nonetheless, some rates of release of adenosine, inosine and hypoxanthine from organs and tissues subjected to various conditions are

TABLE 6

Rates of adenosine, inosine and hypoxanthine release from tissues

Animal	Tissue	Treatment of animal or tissue	Basal rate of release (nmol min⁻¹ g⁻¹ wet wt.)		Stimulated rate of release (nmol min⁻¹ g⁻¹ wet wt.)	
			Adenosine	Adenosine and inosine and hypoxanthine	Adenosine	Adenosine and inosine and hypoxanthine
Rat	Perfused heart[15]	10 min anoxia	0	1·5	65	180
Guinea-pig	Perfused heart[16]	15 min hypoxia	0·02	0·3	1·8	4·5
Cat	Perfused heart[16]	15 min hypoxia	0·001	0·2	0·3	1·7
Dog	Heart[17]	After 30–60 s ischaemia	—	—	0·13	7·2
Rat	Perfused hind limb[19]	12 min after stimulation for 3 min	>0·01	0·35	0·06	0·97
Dog	Perfused calf muscle[10]	2 min stimulation	−0·01*	0·04	0·02	0·06
Guinea-pig	Brain neocortex slices[126]	10 min stimulation	0·1	—	6	16

* Negative sign indicates uptake.

compiled in Table 6. The rates presented represent the difference between rates of release and re-uptake.

The lowest rates of release are obtained when tissues are adequately supplied with oxygen and an oxidizable substrate. Release from guinea-pig cerebral cortex is increased by anoxia, omission of glucose from the superfusing medium, electrical stimulation, depolarizing agents (ouabain, veratridine, K^+) or certain drugs[46,115] (e.g. chlorpromazine, amylobarbitone). Release from the heart is increased by ischaemia, hypoxia, uncouplers of oxidative phosphorylation, electrical stimulation[116] and adrenaline.[117] (Electrical stimulation and adrenaline may act merely by increasing the requirement of the heart for oxygen.) Release from skeletal muscle,[10] kidney[118,119] and adipose tissue[120] is increased following a period of ischaemia and by sympathetic nerve stimulation. Except perhaps for sympathetic stimulation, all these conditions raise the tissue content of AMP, lower the ATP to ADP concentration ratio and raise the extracellular concentration of K^+. Therefore these data are consistent with the control of mechanisms discussed above but they do not indicate the relative importance of the various mechanisms.

(2) Rates of phosphorylation and deamination of adenosine

There are few data on the effects of different physiological conditions on rates of phosphorylation and deamination of adenosine by tissues which would test those parts of the theory of control of adenosine concentration that refer to rates of utilization. At low concentrations (<5 μM) most of the adenosine is phosphorylated but at higher concentrations a greater proportion is deaminated.[26] Inhibition of transport reduces deamination more than phosphorylation because the intracellular concentration of adenosine is reduced.[121] These findings are consistent with the hypothesis of the control of adenosine concentration by the kinetic properties of adenosine kinase and adenosine deaminase and especially the role of the substrate cycle.

Some workers have suggested that, at low concentrations, most of the adenosine is phosphorylated because the location of the kinase is adjacent to the transport mechanism.[18,31,35,78] However, these workers did not consider the maximal activities and K_m values of the kinase and deaminase in cell-free systems. Moreover, the proportion of adenosine that is phosphorylated may be greater than that predicted from both the properties of the kinase and deaminase and the concentration of exogenous adenosine, since the intracellular concentration of adenosine is sometimes less than the extracellular concentration—see Section III.

V. Physiological Effects of Adenosine

The first hint that adenosine modifies physiological processes came in 1929 when Drury & Szent-Gyorgi observed that injection of adenosine into mammals lowered the arterial blood pressure, dilated the coronary arterioles, induced sleep and inhibited movements of the small intestine.[122]

During the following thirty years more attention was given to the pharmacological effects of adenine nucleotides than those of adenosine. In particular, attention was centred upon ATP, which had not been available in large quantities at the time of Drury's work. Upon injection, ATP produces a state of shock with lowered blood pressure, lowered body temperature, renal dysfunction, mobilization of glycogen from liver and muscle and elevated blood levels of glucose, lactate and pyruvate. This suggested that the release of ATP from damaged tissues contributed to traumatic shock.[123] Although adenosine produced similar effects to ATP, the tissue content of adenosine was considerably less than that of ATP so that it was considered to be less important. If the rapidity of the breakdown of extracellular ATP to adenosine had been appreciated, the nucleoside might have assumed a greater importance in these early studies.

The possibility that adenosine (or adenine nucleotides) is involved in the aetiology of shock is no longer accepted, but there are now a large number of physiological and biochemical processes that are known to be modulated by adenosine. Perhaps the most investigated effect of adenosine is on the rate of blood flow. In 1936, Drury[124] suggested that adenosine may be involved in the control of blood flow but this possibility has only been intensively investigated since about 1960.

A. EFFECTS OF ADENOSINE ON VASCULAR SMOOTH MUSCLE

Physiological concentrations of adenosine cause vasodilation in a number of mammalian organs, including the heart, skeletal muscle, brain, intestine and adipose tissue.[12,125,126] In contrast, adenosine produces vasoconstriction in the kidney[127] and liver.[128] Berne and co-workers have proposed that the vaso-dilatory effects provide the basis for a role of adenosine in the local control of blood flow in relation to the oxygen needs of certain tissues. A decrease in demand for oxygen by a tissue (e.g. due to decreased rate of metabolic work) causes vasoconstriction and reduced blood flow. On the other hand, a period of arterial occlusion is usually followed by increased blood flow (i.e. reactive hyperaemia), which makes more oxygen available to the tissue. Similarly, exercise produces hyperaemia in skeletal muscle with the result that more oxygen is available for the increased aerobic metabolism. These responses are not dependent on a nerve supply, so that they must be mediated by the release of vasoactive chemicals in response to the oxygen delivery. The phenomenon of autoregulation, which ensures that blood flow through certain organs (e.g. heart) fluctuates little in response to changes in arterial blood pressure, may also be mediated by the release of vasoactive chemicals.[125]

Berne[129] has proposed that a deficiency of oxygen increases the rate of release of adenosine from the muscle cells of mammalian heart. Adenosine causes relaxation of the smooth muscle of the coronary arterioles, which results in vasodilation and an increased blood flow to the heart muscle. Thus more oxygen is made available. Some of the evidence in support of this theory is as follows.

1. There are positive correlations between the rate of release of adenosine (and its metabolites) from a perfused heart, the concentration of myocardial adenosine, the rate of coronary blood flow and the degree of cardiac hypoxia. Moreover the rate of release of adenosine in response to hypoxia is sufficient to produce the degree of vasodilation caused by the hypoxia.[130]
2. A small physiological reduction in oxygen supply to the heart causes a rapid rise in the myocardial adenosine level and enhances the rate of release of adenosine to the extracellular compartment.[8]
3. Some compounds which block adenosine uptake and raise its concentration in the extracellular compartment of the heart are effective as coronary vasodilator drugs. Furthermore, at least one such drug, dipyridamole, prolongs reactive hyperaemia in the heart.[131,132]
4. Aminophylline (theophylline ethylenediamine) reduces the effects of both adenosine and reactive hyperaemia on blood flow in the isolated perfused rabbit heart.[133,134]

Berne and co-workers have extended this role of adenosine to other organs on the basis of similar, though less extensive, evidence to that described above. The concentration of adenosine and its rate of release is increased in exercising skeletal muscle (Tables 1 and 6). Since theophylline reduces and dipyridamole prolongs vasodilation in response to both adenosine and exercise,[131,135] it is probable that adenosine mediates exercise hyperaemia. Furthermore, adenosine may be responsible for reactive hyperaemia in skeletal muscle, since the rate of release of adenosine (or a closely related compound) is increased in this condition[136] and it is prolonged by dipyridamole.[131] Similar evidence implicates adenosine in the control of blood flow in brain[11,12] and adipose tissue.[120,126]

Exogenous adenosine produces vasoconstriction in the kidney, in contrast to muscle, brain and adipose tissue. The concentration of adenosine in the kidney rises during occlusion of the renal artery, so that adenosine may be responsible for the period of vasoconstriction which follows such occlusion.[118] It is possible that the release of adenosine in a poorly oxygenated region of the kidney reduces blood flow in that region so that blood is diverted to a well-oxygenated region of the organ, in which the processes of filtration and reabsorption can proceed. It could be suggested that adenosine plays a similar role in the lung, since acute alveolar hypoxia causes local vasoconstriction and this diverts blood to regions of the lung that are adequately oxygenated. However, whilst Bennet & Drury[137] reported that adenosine is a pulmonary vasoconstrictor, Mentzer et al.[14] observed vasodilation. The latter workers suggested that adenosine may, in fact, reduce the pressor response to hypoxia.

It should be emphasized that adenosine is by no means the only vasoactive chemical that has been proposed to mediate the vascular responses described above. Other vasoactive chemicals include ATP[19] and K$^+$,[136] which are especially implicated in skeletal muscle, H$^+$, which is mainly implicated in the brain,[11] and prostaglandins, which may play an important role in the kidney.[38]

B. EFFECTS OF ADENOSINE ON NON-VASCULAR SMOOTH MUSCLE

Adenosine affects other smooth muscle apart from that of the vasculature. It causes relaxation of bronchiolar muscles, the urinary bladder and mammalian gut, whereas it causes contraction of the gut of lower vertebrates, but different species vary in their response of uterine muscle to adenosine. ATP produces similar responses to adenosine except in the urinary bladder.[139]

Burnstock[139-141] has shown that stimulation of non-adrenergic, non-cholinergic nerves supplying a number of smooth muscles produces responses which are, in most respects, mimicked by ATP and usually by adenosine. He has proposed that these "purinergic" nerves release ATP, which interacts with receptors on the smooth muscle to cause relaxation and contraction. The effect of ATP is terminated by degradation to ADP, AMP and adenosine. The adenosine is taken back into the nerve ending.

There is no doubt that the molecule stored in and released by the purinergic nerve ending is ATP. However, there is evidence that adenosine, which is derived from the released ATP, makes an important contribution to the overall effect of purinergic nerve stimulation. First, dipyridamole and hexobendine (inhibitors of adenosine uptake) potentiate inhibition of gut motility by adenosine, ATP or purinergic nerve stimulation.[142] Secondly, adenosine and ATP are equally effective in causing relaxation in some smooth muscle preparations. Half-maximal responses are produced by concentrations around 1 μM. (A problem in the comparison of the effects of adenosine and ATP is that the adenosine concentration can be rapidly lowered owing to uptake and metabolism in the tissue—see Section III. This problem can be avoided by the inclusion of an inhibitor of adenosine transport in the system.)[142,143] Thirdly, it has been observed that adenosine deaminase produces a strong contraction of rat or guinea-pig jejunum in vitro, which suggests that adenosine is normally causing relaxation of the muscle.[144] This adenosine could be derived either from ATP released by purinergic nerves or from intracellular AMP.

C. EFFECTS OF ADENOSINE ON NERVOUS TISSUE AND THE HEART

Effects of adenosine on nervous tissue have been observed in three experimental situations. First, in the intact animal, adenosine antagonizes morphine-induced analgesia, prevents convulsions and assists learning.[145] Adenosine also induces sleep.[66,122,146]

In support of the role of adenosine in the induction of sleep is the observation that the concentration of adenosine in rat brain is elevated if the animals are deprived of paradoxical sleep.[146] As an extension of its possible role in sleep, adenosine can be implicated in hypoglycaemic coma: a deficiency of glucose increases the rate of release of adenosine from brain slices.

A second experimental situation involves the application of very small quantities of adenosine to neurones by the technique of micro-iontophoresis. Adenosine greatly depresses the electrical activity of cerebral, cerebellar and olfactory cortical neurones.[147,148] Inhibitors of adenosine transport or adenosine deaminase activity prolong the effect of adenosine. Indeed, inhibition of the enzyme adenosine deaminase depresses the spontaneous activity of cerebral cortical neurones, which suggests that adenosine is released endogenously.[147] Since adenosine is also released from electrically stimulated brain slices (see Section IV), it may be an inhibitory neurotransmitter in the brain. Another possibility is that there are purinergic nerves in the brain, which release ATP. However, even if ATP is the molecule released, it appears that it must be hydrolysed to adenosine by ectoenzymes before it produces its inhibitory effect, since analogues of ATP that cannot be hydrolysed are ineffective.[147]

In a third type of experiment, physiological concentrations of adenosine have been found to inhibit the release of noradrenaline from electrically-stimulated blood vessels[149,150] and nervous-stimulated kidney, adipose tissue and vas deferens.[126] Adenosine also inhibits the release of acetylcholine at the neuromuscular junctions of the rat diaphragm and frog sartorius muscle.[151] There is some evidence that endogenous adenosine inhibits noradrenaline release: dialzep, which inhibits adenosine uptake, reduces contraction of rat portal vein in response to electrical stimulation.[150]

In common with the other effects of adenosine on excitable tissues, ATP is at least as potent as the nucleoside as an inhibitor of neurotransmitter release. Thus the source of adenosine *in vivo* may be ATP and the source of the ATP may be purinergic nerves. Alternatively, the ATP that is associated with the transmitters in adrenergic and cholinergic nerves may serve a transmitter function, though this suggestion is contrary to classical pharmacological concepts.[57]

The inhibitory effects of adenosine on nervous tissue may be related to its effects on the contraction of the heart. Adenosine slows or stops the heart in the frog, turtle, oyster and several mammalian species.[64,139,152] These effects are mediated primarily by inhibition of the electrical activity of the sinus node.[139] There is evidence that endogenous adenosine regulates the heart rate since dipyridamole and dialzep both slow the rate of the dog sino-atrial node preparation in the absence of exogenous adenosine.[153] However, the source of the endogenous adenosine and the physiological significance of its effect is unclear. (Purinergic nerves have not been detected in the heart.[139])

Not all the effects of adenosine on excitable tissues are inhibitory. Some gastropod hearts are stimulated by as little as 0.01 μM adenosine.[154] In view of this finding and the observation that some insect flight muscles contain very high activities of adenosine kinase,[26] the physiological role of adenosine in invertebrate tissues deserves further investigation.

D. EFFECTS OF ADENOSINE ON LIPOLYSIS AND GLUCOSE OXIDATION IN ADIPOSE TISSUE

There is considerable biochemical interest in the effect of adenosine on lipolysis in adipose tissue. In the presence of adrenaline or noradrenaline, adipocytes release adenosine, which inhibits lipolysis by 50% at a concentration of 0.01 μM.[155,156] The addition of adenosine deaminase to the adipocytes increases basal and prolongs hormone-stimulated lipolysis. It should be noted that papaverine and dipyridamole inhibit lipolysis, *in vitro*, despite the fact that they are potent inhibitors of cyclic AMP phosphodiesterase and therefore should increase lipolysis.[157,158] This may be explained by an increase in the concentration of adenosine in the medium, since both compounds inhibit adenosine uptake.

It is important to consider the possibility that the physiological significance of the adenosine effect on fat cells may not be the inhibition of lipolysis *per se*. Perhaps the important role of adenosine is to prevent a large increase in the concentration of cyclic AMP in the adipocytes. Maximal rates of lipolysis require a relatively small increase in cyclic AMP concentration,[157,159] so that any further increase may be undesirable: it would increase the time needed for the tissue to respond to a reduction in the concentration of the lipolytic hormone and thereby reduce or prevent the antilipolytic effect of insulin.[160] It is interesting to note that adenosine inhibits hormone-stimulated cyclic AMP production to a greater extent than the increase in lipolysis.[159,161]

In addition to its antilipolytic effect, adenosine both mimics and potentiates the stimulation of glucose oxidation by insulin in adipose tissue. The effect is seen at concentrations of adenosine as low as 0.01 μM.[160] Other agents that lower the cyclic AMP content of adipose tissue also potentiate the insulin effect on glucose oxidation.[156] It is tempting to speculate that inhibition of excessive cyclic AMP accumulation by adenosine is necessary in order for insulin to increase glucose oxidation (and perhaps also lipogenesis).

E. EFFECTS OF ADENOSINE ON PLATELET AGGREGATION AND ON OTHER BLOOD CELLS

Low concentrations of adenosine (approximately $0 \cdot 1$ μM) inhibit platelet aggregation, whether it is produced *in vitro* by addition of biochemicals, such as ADP or thrombin, or *in vivo* by a mechanical procedure, such as pinching a blood vessel.[162,163] Dipyridamole interacts synergistically with exogenous adenosine to inhibit platelet aggregation *in vitro*[163] and it also inhibits platelet aggregation when added alone—possibly through an increase in the concentration of endogenous adenosine.[164] Moreover, dipyridamole inhibits thrombus formation *in vivo*.[165,166]

The antithrombitic effect of dipyridamole may be due to potentiation of an antithrombitic effect of endogenous adenosine, since the adenosine concentration in the blood is sufficient to inhibit platelet aggregation *in vitro*. Thus adenosine may play a physiological role in the regulation of platelet aggregation: its release from inadequately oxygenated tissues should inhibit thrombus formation and thereby prevent any further reduction in oxygen supply.

Platelets are not the only blood cells whose function is affected by physiological concentrations of adenosine—lymphocyte and lymphoblast proliferation is inhibited by adenosine,[167] whereas red cell production (erythropoiesis) is stimulated.[168] These effects may be of physiological significance. Thus the rate of erythropoiesis increases during hypoxia, a condition which may be expected to raise the concentration of adenosine in the bone marrow. Circumstantial evidence implicating adenosine in the regulation of lymphocyte transformation is derived from the following observations.[167,169,170] First, the activity of adenosine deaminase is especially high in lymphocytes and in tissues with a high content of lymphoid cells. Secondly, even higher activities are present in the blast cells of patients suffering from lymphoblastic leukaemia and in the plasma blasts that are discharged into the circulation during a normal immune response. This suggests that adenosine concentrations are lowered during lymphocyte proliferation. Thirdly, a number of cases of congenital immunodeficiency have been described in which lymphocyte number is very low and the activity of adenosine deaminase in erythrocytes (and perhaps other tissues) is not detectable. The concentration of adenosine in plasma from at least one of these patients has been shown to be elevated.[21]

F. EFFECTS OF ADENOSINE ON OTHER ASPECTS OF METABOLISM AND ENDOCRINOLOGY

Many authors have used adenosine as a tool with which to modify intracellular adenine nucleotide concentrations. High doses (at least 160 μmol kg^{-1} body wt.) or high concentrations (at least 100 μM) of adenosine inhibit gluconeogenesis, lipogenesis and fatty acid oxidation in liver.[171,172,173] Rather more physiological significance may be attached to reports that adenosine stimulates steroid production by adrenal cells,[174] raises plasma corticosterone levels[175] and inhibits insulin production by isolated islets of Langerhans.[176] The latter effect was obtained with as little as 0·1 μM adenosine. Thus, adenosine may modulate hormone release, though to what purpose is not apparent.

There is little doubt that many physiological effects of adenosine remain to be discovered. The reader may feel that adenosine cannot have so many roles as suggested in this Essay. However, such a plethora of effects has been progressively discovered for many other messenger molecules (e.g. noradrenaline, cyclic AMP). There may be a limit to the number of compounds that can perform the role of a messenger molecule due to the problems inherent in the steady-state system necessary to maintain a precise concentration of the messenger. Consequently, once such a messenger has evolved, there may have been considerable evolutionary pressure to utilize it in as many ways as possible. These same pressures may have resulted in the evolution of two types of receptor for adenosine: one mediating excitatory and the other inhibitory responses.[141] The presence of these receptors in different proportions in different tissues and species may explain why adenosine relaxes many smooth muscles but contracts the vascular muscle of liver and kidney and uterine muscle of the guinea-pig, and why it inhibits the electrical activity of hearts from the frog, turtle, oyster and several mammals but it stimulates gastropod hearts. These differences have many parallels in biology. For example, α- and β-adrenergic receptors mediate opposing effects on lipolysis and vascular tone.

VI. Mechanisms of Action of Adenosine

The various effects of adenosine may be achieved through changes in concentration of cyclic AMP, cyclic GMP or other adenine nucleotides or through changes in the distribution of certain cations. The evidence for the mechanism of action of adenosine in different tissues is outlined below.

A. CHANGES IN ATP, ADP AND AMP LEVELS

Exogenous adenosine raises the contents of AMP, ADP and especially ATP in a number of tissues,[172,173,177] but there are also reports that it does not raise the adenine nucleotide level[35,178] or it raises the level only when the latter has been depleted.[177]

The concentration of adenosine used for these studies has either been high (greater than 0·5 mM or 160 μmol kg^{-1} body wt.) or the tissue has been incubated in a large volume of medium compared to its own size. Therefore it is likely that the elevation in adenine nucleotide content of the tissues can be accounted for by the incorporation of adenosine into adenine nucleotides and is not due to an allosteric effect of adenosine. A proportion of the adenosine may be degraded to hypoxanthine and ribose 1-phosphate via the adenosine deaminase reaction, and the ribose moiety provides an oxidizable substrate which generates the energy required for adenine nucleotide synthesis.[179]

B. CHANGES IN CYCLIC NUCLEOTIDE LEVELS

In 1970, Sattin & Rall[180] reported that exogenous adenosine increased the cyclic AMP content of guinea-pig cerebral cortex slices by 20- to 30-fold. Physiological concentrations of adenosine raise cyclic AMP levels in many other tissues, including lymphocytes and platelets.[181-187] The cyclic AMP content of thyroid gland[180] and smooth muscle,[188] is increased but only when adenosine is present at a concentration of at least 0·5 mM. Fat cells are exceptional in that adenosine reduces the concentration of cyclic AMP (see Section V.D). This may be due to the presence of a different type of receptor to that in brain, lymphocytes and platelets (see Section V.F).

In most, if not all of these tissues, adenosine changes cyclic AMP levels by allosteric modulation of adenylate cyclase activity. Thus the rate of formation of [^{14}C]cyclic AMP from [^{14}C]ATP, which is pre-labelled by incubation of the tissue with [^{14}C]adenine or [^{14}C]adenosine, is markedly increased by adenosine (unlabelled).[181,184] (The rate is decreased in fat cells.[159]) The possibility that adenosine increases cyclase activity by increasing the ATP concentration in the vicinity of the enzyme has been excluded by the finding that analogues of adenosine that are not converted to ATP (e.g. 2-chloroadenosine, N^6-benzyladenosine) also lead to a stimulation of the cyclase activity.[181]

Despite this evidence of the action of adenosine on cyclase activity with intact cell preparations, it has been more difficult to demonstrate an effect on enzyme activity in cell-free systems. Adenosine increases the activity of adenylate cyclase in cell-free extracts of human platelets[189] and cultured glioma cells[190] but, in order to demonstrate the effect in cell free extracts of brain, it is essential that no endogenous adenosine is present in the extract and that adenosine is not produced from the hydrolysis of the ATP which is added as substrate for the enzyme.[191]

Adenosine probably stimulates (or in fat cells inhibits) the activity of adenylate cyclase by interacting with a receptor that resides on the external side of the plasma membrane (in an analogous manner to the proposed action of some hormones). Thus adenosine need not enter the cell to modify the activity of adenylate cyclase. In support of this are the observations that inhibition of adenosine uptake potentiates the effect on cyclic AMP levels,[183,186,187,192] and this effect is blocked by some adenosine analogues (e.g. 2'-deoxyadenosine[181]). Methylxanthines may also compete for the adenosine receptor, since they reduce, in a competitive manner, the effect of adenosine on cyclic AMP levels and adenylate cyclase activity.[180,187,191,193] However, this is not conclusive evidence for competition at a single receptor.[183,194]

Adenosine increases cyclic GMP as well as cyclic AMP levels in guinea-pig brain slices.[195,196] The effect is potentiated by papaverine and blocked by theophylline but, unlike the effect on cyclic AMP levels, it is not blocked by deoxyadenosine.[195] Thus the receptors that mediate the increases in the levels of cyclic GMP and cyclic AMP may be different.

C. RELATIONSHIP BETWEEN BIOCHEMICAL CHANGES AND PHYSIOLOGICAL EFFECTS

Most of the effects of adenosine cannot be dependent on the conversion of adenosine to adenine nucleotides, since they are potentiated by inhibitors of adenosine uptake, and there is evidence that cyclic AMP mediates some of these effects. For example, although platelet aggregation can be affected by factors other than cyclic AMP, there is strong evidence that inhibition of aggregation by adenosine is somehow mediated by the increase in cyclic AMP level.[197] Similarly, inhibition of lymphocyte function by adenosine is associated with elevated levels of cyclic AMP and since dibutyryl cyclic AMP inhibits both the proliferation and action of lymphocytes, the adenosine effect may be mediated by cyclic AMP.[167] Furthermore, steroid production in adrenal cells[174] and erythropoiesis are also stimulated by dibutyryl cyclic AMP.[168]

It has already been noted that the mechanism of inhibition of lipolysis by adenosine is unusual since it involves inhibition of adenylate cyclase activity. Inhibition of insulin secretion by adenosine may also be mediated by inhibition of cyclase activity in the β-cell of the islets of Langerhans. Thus adenosine inhibits β-cell cyclase activity in vitro and dibutyryl cyclic AMP produces the opposite effect to adenosine, i.e. stimulation of insulin release.[176]

However, it is very unlikely that all the physiologically important effects of adenosine can be explained by changes in the concentration of cyclic AMP. Notably, relaxation of vascular or non-vascular smooth muscle by adenosine has not been correlated with changes in cyclic AMP levels.[188,198] (This is an unexpected result since, like the cyclic-AMP-mediated effects, relaxation is produced by the interaction of adenosine with an extracellular receptor and the effect is blocked by theophylline.[194]) It is possible that the effect of adenosine on smooth muscle is mediated by a decrease in permeability to K^+ or Na^+.[198]

D. CONFUSION RESULTING FROM THE EFFECTS OF PHOSPHODIESTERASE INHIBITORS ON ADENOSINE ACTION

In some instances it has been tacitly assumed that the effects of papaverine and dipyridamole, which inhibit adenosine transport, and caffeine and theophylline, which block the effects of adenosine, are due to inhibition of phosphodiesterase activity. The major effects of these compounds are likely to be due to their actions on the adenosine system. Thus it is improbable that, in most *in vivo* studies, these compounds reach a sufficient concentration to inhibit phosphodiesterase, but they may reach a sufficient concentration to affect the adenosine system. Without further experimental evidence we consider that the phosphodiesterase mechanism is not proven.

REFERENCES

1. Bodansky, O. & Schwartz, M. J. (1968). 5'-Nucleotidase. *Adv. Clin. Chem.* **11**, 277–328.
2. György, P. & Röthler, H. (1927). Über Bedingungen der autolytischen Ammoniakbildung in Geweben. *Biochem. Z.* **187**, 194–219.
3. Lowy, B. A., Davoll, J. & Brown, G. B. (1952). The utilization of purine nucleosides for nucleic acid synthesis in the rat. *J. Biol. Chem.* **197**, 591–600.
4. Caputto, R. (1951). The enzymatic synthesis of adenylic acid; adenosine kinase. *J. Biol. Chem.* **189**, 801–814.
5. Kornberg, A. & Pricer, W. E. (1951). Enzymatic phosphorylation of adenosine and 2,6-diaminopurine riboside. *J. Biol. Chem.* **193**, 481–495.
6. Buchanan, J. M. (1960). The enzymatic synthesis of the purine nucleotides. *The Harvey Lectures* **54**, 104–130.
7. Kornberg, A. (1957). Pathways of enzymatic synthesis of nucleotides and polynucleotides. In *The Chemical Basis of Heredity* (McElroy, W. D. & Glass, B., eds). Johns Hopkins, Baltimore, pp. 579–608.
8. Berne, R. M. & Rubio, R. (1974). Adenine nucleotide metabolism in the heart. *Circ. Res. Suppl. III* to **34** and **35**, 109–120.
9. Rubio, R., Berne, R. M. & Dobson, J. G. (1973). Sites of adenosine production in cardiac and skeletal muscle. *Amer. J. Physiol.* **225**, 938–953.
10. Bockman, E. L., Berne, R. M. & Rubio, R. (1976). Adenosine and active hyperaemia in dog skeletal muscle. *Amer. J. Physiol.* **230**, 1531–1537.
11. Rubio, R., Berne, R. M., Bockman, E. L. & Curnish, R. R. (1975). Relationship between adenosine concentrations and oxygen supply in rat brain. *Amer. J. Physiol.* **228**, 1896–1902.
12. Berne, R. M., Rubio, R. & Curnish, R. R. (1974). Release of adenosine from ischaemic brain. Effect on cerebral vascular resistance and incorporation into cerebral adenine nucleotides. *Circ. Res.* **35**, 262–271.
13. Newman, M. & McIlwain, H. (1977). Adenosine as a constituent of the brain and of isolated cerebral tissues and its relationship to the generation of adenosine 3':5'-cyclic monophosphate. *Biochem. J.* **164**, 131–137.
14. Mentzer, R. M., Rubio, R. & Berne, R. M. (1975). Release of adenosine by hypoxic canine lung tissue and its possible role in pulmonary circulation. *Amer. J. Physiol.* **229**, 1625–1631.

15. Frick, G. P. & Lowenstein, J. M. (1976). Studies of 5'-nucleotidase in the perfused rat heart. *J. Biol. Chem.* **251**, 6372–6378.
16. Katori, M. & Berne, R. M. (1966). Release of adenosine from anoxic hearts. Relationship to coronary flow. *Circ. Res.* **19**, 420–425.
17. Rubio, R., Berne, R. N. & Katori, M. (1969). Release of adenosine in reactive hyperaemia of the dog heart. *Amer. J. Physiol.* **216**, 56–62.
18. Rubio, R. & Berne, R. M. (1969). Release of adenosine by the normal myocardium in dogs and its relationship to the regulation of coronary resistance. *Circ. Res.* **25**, 407–415.
19. Bockman, E. L., Berne, R. M. & Rubio, R. (1975). Release of adenosine and lack of release of ATP from contracting skeletal muscle. *Pflügers Arch.* **355**, 229–241.
20. Dobson, J. G., Rubio, R. & Berne, R. M. (1971). Role of adenine nucleotides, adenosine, and inorganic phosphate in the regulation of skeletal muscle blood flow. *Circ. Res.* **29**, 375–384.
21. Mills, G. C., Schmalstieg, F. C., Trimmer, K. B., Goldman, A. S. & Goldblum, R. M. (1976). Purine metabolism in adenosine deaminase deficiency. *Proc. Natl. Acad. Sci. U.S.* **73**, 2867–2871.
22. Fernley, H. N. (1971). Mammalian alkaline phosphatases. In *The Enzymes*, Vol. 4 (Boyer, P. D., ed.). Academic Press, New York and London, pp. 417–447.
23. Hollander, V. P. (1971). Acid phosphatases. In *The Enzymes*, Vol. 4 (Boyer, P. D., ed.). Academic Press, New York and London, pp. 449–498.
24. Murray, A. W., Elliot, D. C. & Atkinson, M. R. (1970). Nucleotide biosynthesis from preformed purines in mammalian cells: regulatory mechanisms and biological significance. *Progr. Nucleic Acid Res. Mol. Biol.* **10**, 87–119.
25. Drummond, G. I. & Yamamoto, M. (1971). Nucleotide phosphomonoesterases. In *The Enzymes*, Vol. 4 (Boyer, P. D., ed.). Academic Press, New York and London, pp. 337–371.
26. Arch, J. R. S. & Newsholme, E. A. (1978). Activities and some properties of 5'-nucleotidase, adenosine kinase and adenosine deaminase in tissues from vertebrates and invertebrates in relation to the control of the concentration and the physiological role of adenosine. *Biochem. J.* **174**, 965–977.
27. Santos, J. N., Hempstead, K. W., Kopp, L. E. & Miech, R. P. (1968). Nucleotide metabolism in rat brain. *J. Neurochem.* **15**, 367–376.
28. Holmsen, H. & Rozenberg, M. C. (1968). Adenine nucleotide metabolism of blood platelets. I. Adenosine kinase and nucleotide formation from exogenous adenosine and AMP. *Biochim. Biophys. Acta* **155**, 326–341.
29. Maguire, M. H., Lukas, M. C. & Rettie, J. F. (1972). Adenine nucleotide salvage synthesis in the rat heart; pathways of adenosine salvage. *Biochim. Biophys. Acta* **262**, 108–115.
30. Lowy, B. A. & Williams, M. K. (1966). Studies on the metabolism of adenosine and adenine in stored and fresh human erythrocytes. *Blood* **27**, 623–628.
31. Liu, M. S. & Feinberg, H. (1971). Incorporation of adenosine-8-^{14}C and inosine-8-^{14}C into rabbit heart adenosine nucleotides. *Amer. J. Physiol.* **220**, 1242–1248.
32. De Jong, J. W. & Kalkman, C. (1973). Myocardial adenosine kinase: activity and localization determined with rapid radiometric assay. *Biochim. Biophys. Acta* **320**, 388–396.
33. Goldthwaite, D. A. (1957). Mechanisms of synthesis of purine nucleotides in heart muscle extracts. *J. Clin. Invest.* **36**, 1572–1578.
34. Wiedmeier, V. T., Rubio, R. & Berne, R. M. (1972). Incorporation and turnover

of adenosine-U-^{14}C in perfused guinea pig myocardium. *Amer. J. Physiol.* **223**, 51–54.

35. Shimizu, H., Tanaka, S. & Kodama, T. (1972). Adenosine kinase of mammalian brain: partial purification and its role for the uptake of adenosine. *J. Neurochem.* **19**, 687–698.

36. Wiedmeier, V. T., Rubio, R. & Berne, R. M. (1972). Inosine incorporation into myocardial nucleotides. *J. Mol. Cell. Cardiol.* **4**, 445–452.

37. Lerner, M. H. & Rubinstein, D. (1970). The role of adenine and adenosine as precursors for adenine nucleotide synthesis by fresh and preserved human erythrocytes. *Biochim. Biophys. Acta.* **224**, 301–310.

38. Bosmann, H. B. & Hemsworth, B. A. (1970). Intraneural mitochondria. Incorporation of amino acids and monosaccharides into macromolecules by isolated synaptosomes and synaptosomal mitochondria. *J. Biol. Chem.* **245**, 363–371.

39. DePierre, J. W. & Karnovsky, M. L. (1973). Plasma membranes of mammalian cells. A review of methods for their characterization and isolation. *J. Cell Biol.* **56**, 275–303.

40. Ryan, J. W. & Smith, U. (1971). Metabolism of adenosine 5′-monophosphate during circulation through the lungs. *Trans. Assoc. Amer. Physicians* **84**, 297–306.

41. Naidoo, D. (1962). The activity of 5′-nucleotidase determined histochemically in the developing rat brain. *J. Histochem. Cytochem.* **10**, 421–434.

42. Barron, K. D. & Bernsohn, J. (1965). Brain esterases and phosphatases in multiple sclerosis. *Ann. N.Y. Acad. Sci.* **122**, 369–399.

43. Essner, E., Novikoff, A. B. & Masek, B. (1958). Adenosinetriphosphatase and 5′-nucleotidase activities in the plasma membrane of liver cells as revealed by electron microscopy. *J. Biophys. Biochem. Cytol.* **4**, 711–716.

44. Gurd, J. W. & Evans, W. H. (1974). Distribution of liver plasma membrane 5′-nucleotidase as indicated by its reaction with anti-plasma membrane serum. *Arch. Biochem. Biophys.* **164**, 305–311.

45. Newby, A. C., Luzio, J. P. & Hales, N. C. (1975). The properties and extracellular location of 5′-nucleotidase of the rat fat-cell plasma membrane. *Biochem. J.* **146**, 625–633.

46. Pull, I. & McIlwain, H. (1972). Metabolism of [^{14}C]adenine and derivatives by cerebral tissues, superfused and electrically stimulated. *Biochem. J.* **126**, 965–973.

47. Trams, E. G. & Lauter, C. J. (1974). On the sidedness of plasma membrane enzymes. *Biochim. Biophys. Acta* **345**, 180–197.

48. Gorin, E. & Brenner, T. (1976). Extracellular metabolism of cyclic AMP. *Biochim. Biophys. Acta* **451**, 20–28.

49. Phillips, E. & Newsholme, E. A. (1979). Maximum activities, properties and distribution of 5′-nucleotidase, adenosine kinase and adenosine deaminase in rat and human brain. *Brain Research* (submitted for publication).

50. Widnell, C. C. (1972). Cytochemical localization of 5′-nucleotidase in subcellular fractions isolated from rat liver. I. The origin of 5′-nucleotidase activity in microsomes. *J. Cell Biol.* **52**, 542–558.

51. Song, C. S. & Kappas, A. (1969). 5′-Nucleotidase of plasma membranes of the rat liver: studies on subcellular distribution. *Ann. N.Y. Acad. Sci.* **166**, 565–573.

52. Baer, H.-P., Drummond, G. I. & Duncan, E. L. (1966). Formation and deamination of adenosine by cardiac muscle enzymes. *Mol. Pharmacol.* **2**, 67–76.

53. Gibson, W. B. & Drummond, G. I. (1972). Properties of 5'-nucleotidase from avian heart. *Biochemistry* **11**, 223–229.

54. Bajusz, E. & Jasmin, G. (1964). Histochemical studies on the myocardium following experimental interference with coronary circulation in the rat. *Acta Histochem. Suppl.* **18**, 222–237.

55. Nakatsu, K. & Drummond, G. I. (1972). Adenylate metabolism and adenosine formation in the heart. *Amer. J. Physiol.* **223**, 1119–1127.

56. Borgers, M., Schaper, J. & Schaper, W. (1971). Adenosine-producing sites in the mammalian heart: a cytochemical study. *J. Mol. Cell. Cardiol.* **3**, 287–296.

57. Burnstock, G. (1976). Do some nerve cells release more than one transmitter? *Neuroscience* **1**, 239–248.

58. Pilkis, S. J., Exton, J. H., Johnson, R. A. & Park, C. R. (1974). Effects of glucagon on cyclic AMP and carbohydrate metabolism in livers from diabetic rats. *Biochim. Biophys. Acta* **343**, 250–267.

59. O'Brien, J. A. & Strange, R. C. (1975). The release of adenosine 3':5'-cyclic monophosphate from the isolated perfused rat heart. *Biochem. J.* **152**, 429–432.

60. Rabinowitz, B., Parmley, W. W., Kligerman, M., Norman, J., Fujimura, S., Chiba, S. & Matloff, J. M. (1975). Myocardial and plasma levels of adenosine 3':5'-cyclic phosphate. Studies in experimental myocardial ischaemia. *Chest* **68**, 69–74.

61. Baer, H. P. & Drummond, G. I. (1968). Catabolism of adenine nucleotides by the isolated perfused rat heart. *Proc. Soc. Exp. Biol. Med.* **127**, 33–36.

62. Zumstein, P., Zapf, J. & Froesch, E. R. (1974). Effects of hormones on cyclic AMP release from rat adipose tissue *in vitro*. *FEBS Lett.* **49**, 65–69.

63. Granner, D. K., Sellers, L., Lee, A., Butters, C. & Kutina, L. (1975). A comparison of the uptake, metabolism, and action of cyclic adenine nucleotides in cultured hepatoma cells. *Arch. Biochem. Biophys.* **169**, 601–615.

64. Robison, G. A., Butcher, R. W. & Sutherland, E. W. (1971). *Cyclic AMP*. Academic Press, New York and London.

65. Solomon, S. S., Brush, J. S. & Kitabchi, A. E. (1970). Divergent biological effects of adenosine and dibutyryl adenosine 3',5'-monophosphate on the isolated fat cell. *Science* **169**, 387–388.

66. Marley, E. & Nistico, G. (1972). Effects of catecholamines and adenosine derivatives given into the brain of fowls. *Br. J. Pharmacol.* **46**, 619–636.

67. Arch, J. R. S. & Newsholme, E. A. (1976). Activities and some properties of adenylate cyclase and phosphodiesterase in muscle, liver and nervous tissues from vertebrates and invertebrates in relation to the control of the concentration of adenosine 3':5'-cyclic monophosphate. *Biochem. J.* **158**, 603–622.

68. Lerner, M. H. & Lowy, B. A. (1974). Formation of adenosine in rabbit liver and its possible role as a direct precursor of erythrocyte adenine nucleotides. *J. Biol. Chem.* **249**, 959–966.

69. Caldwell, I. C., Henderson, J. F. & Paterson, A. R. P. (1966). The enzymic formation of 6-(methylmercapto)purine ribonucleoside 5'-phosphate. *Can. J. Biochem.* **44**, 229–245.

70. Schrader, J., Berne, R. M. & Rubio, R. (1972). Uptake and metabolism of adenosine by human erythrocyte ghosts. *Amer. J. Physiol.* **223**, 159–166.

71. Pull, I. & McIlwain, H. (1974). Rat cerebral-cortex adenosine deaminase activity and its subcellular distribution. *Biochem. J.* **144**, 37–41.

72. Hopkins, S. V. & Goldie, R. G. (1971). A species difference in the uptake of adenosine by heart. *Biochem. Pharmacol.* **20**, 3359–3365.

73. Olsson, R. A., Snow, J. A., Gentry, M. K. & Frick, G. P. (1972). Adenosine uptake by canine heart. *Circ. Res.* **31**, 767–778.

74. Pearson, J. D., Carleton, J. S., Hutchings, A. & Gordon, J. L. (1978). Uptake and metabolism of adenosine by pig aortic endothelial and smooth-muscle cells in culture. *Biochem. J.* **170**, 265–271.

75. Kübler, W. & Bretschneider, H. J. (1963). Die Permeation von Adenosin durch die Erythrocytenmembran des Hundes. *Pflüger Archiv. Physiol.* **277**, 141–149.

76. Scholtissek, C. (1968). Studies on the uptake of nucleic acid precursors into cells in tissue culture. *Biochim. Biophys. Acta* **158**, 435–447.

77. Plagemann, P. G. W. & Richey, D. P. (1974). Transport of nucleosides, nucleic acid bases, choline and glucose by animal cells in culture. *Biochim. Biophys. Acta* **344**, 263–305.

78. Kolassa, N. & Pfleger, K. (1975). Adenosine uptake by erythrocytes of man, rat and guinea-pig and its inhibition by hexobendine and dipyridamole. *Biochem. Pharmacol.* **24**, 154–156.

79. Paterson, A. R. P. & Oliver, J. M. (1971). Nucleoside transport. II. Inhibition by *p*-nitrobenzylthioguanosine and related compounds. *Can. J. Biochem.* **49**, 271–274.

80. Reimers, H.-J., Packham, M. A., Cazenave, J.-P. & Mustard, J. F. (1977). Effect of reserpine on adenosine uptake and metabolism, and subcellular transport of platelet adenosine triphosphate in washed rabbit platelets. *Biochem. Pharmacol.* **26**, 1657–1665.

81. Strauss, P. R., Sheehan, J. M. & Kashket, E. R. (1976). Membrane transport by murine lymphocytes. A rapid sampling technique as applied to the adenosine and thymidine systems. *J. Exp. Med.* **144**, 1009–1021.

82. Plagemann, P. G. W. (1971). Nucleotide pools of Novikoff rat hepatoma cells growing in suspension culture. I. Kinetics of incorporation of nucleosides into nucleotide pools and pool sizes during growth cycle. *J. Cell. Physiol.* **77**, 213–240.

83. Van Belle, H. (1969). Uptake and deamination of adenosine by blood. Species differences, effect of pH, ions, temperature and metabolic inhibitors. *Biochim. Biophys. Acta* **192**, 124–132.

84. Randle, P. J. & Smith, G. H. (1958). The effects of insulin, anaerobiosis and cell poisons on the penetration of the isolated rat diaphragm by sugars. *Biochem. J.* **70**, 501–508.

85. Morgan, H. E., Randle, P. J. & Regen, D. M. (1969). The effects of insulin, anoxia, salicylate and 2 : 4 dinitrophenol on membrane transport and intracellular phosphorylation of glucose in the isolated rat heart. *Biochem. J.* **73**, 573–579.

86. Mustafa, S. J., Rubio, R. & Berne, R. M. (1975). Uptake of adenosine by dispersed chick embryonic cardiac cells. *Amer. J. Physiol.* **228**, 62–67.

87. Meyskens, F. L. & Williams, H. E. (1971). Adenosine metabolism in human erythrocytes. *Biochim. Biophys. Acta* **240**, 170–179.

88. Lindberg, B., Klenow, H. & Hansen, K. (1967). Some properties of partially purified mammalian adenosine kinase. *J. Biol. Chem.* **242**, 350–356.

89. Newsholme, E. A. & Start, C. (1973). *Regulation in Metabolism.* Wiley-Interscience, London, New York, Sydney and Toronto.

90. Crabtree, B. (1976). Theoretical considerations of the sensitivity conferred by substrate cycles *in vivo. Biochem. Soc. Trans.* **4**, 999–1002.

91. Newsholme, E. A. & Crabtree, B. (1976). Substrate cycles in metabolic regulation and in heat generation. *Biochem. Soc. Symp.* **41**, 61–109.

118   J. R. S. ARCH AND E. A. NEWSHOLME

92. West, E. S., Todd, W. R., Mason, H. S. & Van Bruggen, J. T. (1966). *Textbook of Biochemistry.* Collier-Macmillan, London, p. 891.
93. Wolfenden, R. (1967). The free energy of hydrolysis of adenosine to inosine and ammonia. *J. Biol. Chem.* **242**, 4711–4714.
94. Regen, D. M., Davis, W. W., Morgan, H. E. & Park, C. R. (1964). The regulation of hexokinase and phosphofructokinase activity in heart muscle. Effects of alloxan diabetes, growth hormone, cortisol and anoxia. *J. Biol. Chem.* **239**, 43–49.
95. Gerez, G. & Kirsten, R. (1965). Release of ammonia during muscular activity. *Biochem. Z.* **341**, 534–542.
96. Bergmeyer, H. U. (1974). *Methods of Enzymatic Analysis,* Vol. 4, Verlag Chemie Weinheim, Academic Press, New York and London.
97. Newsholme, E. A. & Crabtree, B. (1973). Metabolic aspects of enzyme regulation. *Symp. Soc. Exp. Biol.* **27**, 429–460.
98. Kluge, H., Hartmann, W., Wieczorek, V. & Zahlten, W. (1972). Kinetic properties of cerebral 5′-nucleotidase. *J. Neurochem.* **19**, 1409–1411.
99. Burger, R. M. & Lowenstein, J. M. (1975). 5′-Nucleotidase from smooth muscle of small intestine and brain. Inhibition by nucleotides. *Biochemistry* **14**, 2362–2366.
100. Sullivan, J. M. & Alpers, J. B. (1971). *In vitro* regulation of rat heart 5′-nucleotidase by adenine nucleotides and magnesium. *J. Biol. Chem.* **246**, 3057–3063.
101. Ipata, P. L. (1968). Sheep brain 5-nucleotidase. Some enzymic properties and allosteric inhibition by nucleoside triphosphates. *Biochemistry* **7**, 507–515.
102. Edwards, M. J. & Maguire, M. H. (1970). Purification and properties of rat heart 5′-nucleotidase. *Mol. Pharmacol.* **6**, 641–648.
103. Hoult, D. I., Busby, S. J. W., Gadian, D. G., Radda, G. K., Richards, R. E. & Seeley, P. J. (1974). Observation of tissue metabolites using ^{31}P nuclear magnetic resonance. *Nature (London)* **252**, 285–287.
104. Ma, P. F. & Fisher, J. R. (1966). Adenosine deaminases—some evolutionary trends among vertebrates. *Comp. Biochem. Physiol.* **19**, 799–807.
105. Zielke, C. L. & Sueltter, C. H. (1971). Purine, purine nucleoside, and purine nucleotide aminohydrolases. In *The Enzymes* (Boyer, P. D., ed.). Vol. 4. Academic Press, New York and London, pp. 47–78.
106. Divekar, A. Y. & Hakala, M. T. (1971). Adenosine kinase of Sarcoma 180 cells. [N6]-Substituted adenosines as substrates and inhibitors. *Mol. Pharmacol.* **7**, 663–673.
107. Hiltunen, J. K. & Hassinen, I. E. (1976). Energy-linked regulation of glucose and pyruvate oxidation in isolated perfused rat heart. *Biochim. Biophys. Acta* **440**, 377–390.
108. Elbers, R., Heldt, H. W., Schmuker, P., Soboll, S. & Wiese, H. (1974). Measurement of the ATP/ADP ratio in mitochondria and in the extra-mitochondrial compartment by fractionation of freeze-stopped liver tissue in non-aqueous media. *Hoppe-Seyler's Z. Physiol. Chem.* **355**, 378–393.
109. Faupel, R. P., Seitz, H. J., Tarnowski, W., Thiemann, V. & Weiss, C. H. (1972). The problem of tissue sampling from experimental animals with respect to freezing technique, anoxia, stress and narcosis. A new method for sampling rat liver tissue and the physiological values of glycolytic intermediates and related compounds. *Arch. Biochem. Biophys.* **148**, 509–522.

110. Veech, R. L., Harris, R. L., Veloso, D. & Veech, E. H. (1973). Freeze-blowing: a new technique for the study of brain *in vivo*. *J. Neurochem.* **20**, 183–188.

111. Duling, B. R. (1975). Effects of potassium ion on the microcirculation of the hamster. *Circ. Res.* **37**, 325–332.

112. Pull, I. & McIlwain, H. (1973). Output of [^{14}C] adenine nucleotides and their derivatives from cerebral tissues. *Biochem. J.* **136**, 893–901.

113. Aussedat, J. & Rossi, A. (1977). Conséquences de l'incorporation d'adénosine sur la vitesse de renouvellement des nucleotide adényliques, dans le coeur isolé et perfusé de lapin. *J. Physiol. (Paris)* **73**, 633–652.

114. Pull, I. & McIlwain, H. (1972). Adenine derivatives as neurohumoral agents in the brain. The quantities liberated on excitation of superfused cerebral tissues. *Biochem. J.* **130**, 975–981.

115. Pull, I. & McIlwain, H. (1976). Centrally-acting drugs and related compounds examined for action on output of adenine derivatives from superfused tissues of the brain. *Biochem. Pharmacol.* **25**, 293–297.

116. Watkinson, W. P., Foley, D. H., Rubio, R. & Berne, R. M. (1976). Adenosine production by canine myocardium during stellate ganglion stimulation. *Circulation Suppl. II* to **54**, 107.

117. Richman, H. G. & Wyborny, L. (1964). Adenine nucleotide degradation in the rabbit heart. *Amer. J. Physiol.* **207**, 1139–1145.

118. Thomas, R. A., Rubio, R. & Berne, R. M. (1975). Adenosine metabolism in the kidney: its possible role in the control of renal blood flow. *Fed. Proc. Fed. Am. Soc. Exp. Biol.* **34**, 363.

119. Fredholm, B. B. & Hedqvist, P. (1976). Release of adenosine from the isolated perfused rabbit kidney. *Acta Physiol. Scand. Suppl.* **440**, 68.

120. Fredholm, B. B. (1976). Release of adenosine-like material from isolated perfused dog adipose tissue following sympathetic nerve stimulation and its inhibition by adrenergic α-receptor blockade. *Acta Physiol. Scand.* **96**, 422–430.

121. Agarwal, R. P. & Parks, R. E. (1975). A possible association between the nucleoside transport system of human erythrocytes and adenosine deaminase. *Biochem. Pharmacol.* **24**, 547–550.

122. Drury, A. N. & Szent-Györgyi, A. (1929). The physiological activity of adenine compounds with especial reference to their action upon the mammalian heart. *J. Physiol. (London)* **68**, 213–237.

123. Green, H. N. & Stoner, H. B. (1950). *Biological Actions of the Adenine Nucleotides*. Lewis & Company, London.

124. Drury, A. N. (1936). The physiological activity of nucleic acid and its derivatives. *Physiol. Rev.* **16**, 292–325.

125. Haddy, F. J. & Scott, J. B. (1968). Metabolically linked vasoactive chemicals in local regulation of blood flow. *Physiol. Rev.* **48**, 688–707.

126. Hedqvist, P. & Fredholm, B. B. (1976). Effects of adenosine on adrenergic neurotransmission; prejunctional inhibition and post-junctional enhancement. *Naunyn-Schmiedeberg's Arch. Pharmacol.* **293**, 217–223.

127. Scott, J. B., Daugherty, R. M., Dabney, J. M. & Haddy, F. J. (1965). Role of chemical factors in regulation of flow through kidney, hindlimb and heart. *Amer. J. Physiol.* **208**, 813–824.

128. Hems, D. A. Personal communication.

129. Berne, R. M. (1963). Cardiac nucleotides in hypoxia: possible role in regulation of coronary blood flow. *Amer. J. Physiol.* **204**, 317–322.

130. Rubio, R., Wiedmeier, V. T. & Berne, R. M. (1974). Relationship between coronary flow and adenosine production and release. *J. Mol. Cell. Cardiol.* **6**, 561–566.

131. Muira, M., Tominaga, S. & Hashimoto, K. (1967). Potentiation of reactive hyperaemia in the coronary and femoral circulation by the selective use of 2,6-bis(diethanolamino)-4,8-dipiperidinopyrimido[5,4-d]pyrimidine. *Arzneim. Forsch.* **17**, 976–979.

132. Parratt, J. R. & Wadsworth, R. M. (1972). The effects of dipyridamole on coronary post-occlusion hyperaemia and on myocardial vasodilation induced by systemic hypoxia. *Br. J. Pharmacol.* **46**, 594–601.

133. Blass, K.-E., Zehl, U. & Förster, W. (1976). The influence of adenosine and prostaglandins on regulating processes of cardiac flow: investigations *in vitro* and *in vivo*. *Acta Biol. Med. Ger.* **35**, 1161–1162.

134. Zehl, U. & Förster, W. (1976). Zur Bedeutung von Adenosin und Prostaglandinen für die Koronarregulation des Säugerherzens. *Acta Biol. Med. Ger.* **35**, 517–520.

135. Tabaie, H. M. A., Scott, J. B. & Haddy, F. J. (1977). Reduction of exercise dilation by theophylline. *Proc. Soc. Exp. Biol. Med.* **154**, 93–97.

136. Tominaga, S., Suzuki, T. & Nakamura, T. (1973). Evaluation of roles of potassium, inorganic phosphate, osmolarity, pH, pCO_2, pO_2 and adenosine or AMP in exercise and reactive hyperemias in canine hindlimb muscles. *Tohoku J. Exp. Med.* **109**, 347–363.

137. Bennet, D. W. & Drury, A. N. (1931). Further observations relating to the physiological activity of adenine compounds. *J. Physiol. (London)* **72**, 288–320.

138. Vane, J. R. & McGiff, J. C. (1975). Possible contributions of endogenous prostaglandins to the control of blood pressure. *Circ. Res. Suppl. I* to **36** and **37**, 68–75.

139. Burnstock, G. (1972). Purinergic nerves. *Pharmacol. Rev.* **24**, 509–581.

140. Burnstock, G. (1975). Comparative studies of purinergic nerves. *J. Exp. Zool.* **194**, 103–134.

141. Burnstock, G. (1976). Purinergic receptors. *J. Theor. Biol.* **62**, 491–503.

142. Satchell, D. G. & Burnstock, G. (1975). Comparison of the inhibitory effects on the guinea-pig taenia coli of adenine nucleotides and adenosine in the presence and absence of dipyridamole. *Eur. J. Pharmacol.* **32**, 324–328.

143. Ally, A. I. & Nakatsu, K. (1976). Adenosine inhibition of isolated rabbit ileum and antagonism by theophylline. *J. Pharmacol. Exp. Ther.* **199**, 208–215.

144. Arch, J. R. S., Pearson, J. M. & Wheeler, V. E., Unpublished observations.

145. McIlwain, H. (1976). Translocation of neural modulators: a second category of nerve signal. *Neurochem. Res.* **1**, 351–368.

146. Haulică, I., Ababei, L., Brănişteanu, D. & Topoliceanu, F. (1973). Preliminary data on the possible hypnogenic role of adenosine. *J. Neurochem.* **21**, 1019–1020.

147. Phillis, J. W. & Edstrom, J. P. (1976). Effects of adenosine analogues on rat cerebral cortical neurons. *Life Sci.* **19**, 1041–1053.

148. Kuroda, Y., Saito, M. & Kobayashi, K. (1976). Concomitant changes in cyclic AMP level and postsynaptic potentials of olfactory cortex slices induced by adenosine derivatives. *Brain Res.* **109**, 196–201.

149. Verhaeghe, R. H., Vanhoutte, P. M. & Shepherd, J. T. (1977). Inhibition of sympathetic neurotransmission in canine blood vessels by adenosine and adenine nucleotides. *Circ. Res.* **40**, 208–215.

150. Enero, M. A. & Saidman, B. Q. (1977). Possible feed-back inhibition of noradrenaline release by purine compounds. *Naunyn-Schmiederberg's Arch. Pharmacol.* **297**, 39–46.

151. Ribeiro, J. A. & Walker, J. (1975). The effects of adenosine triphosphate and adenosine diphosphate on transmission at the rat and frog neuromuscular junctions. *Br. J. Pharmacol.* **54**, 213–218.

152. Aikawa, T., Umemori, Y. & Ishida, S. (1967). Effects of adenosine on action potentials in the oyster heart, with special reference to the activity of adenosine aminohydrolase. *Comp. Biochem. Physiol.* **21**, 579–586.

153. Ono, H., Himori, N. & Taira, N. (1977). Chronotropic effects of coronary vasodilators as assessed in the isolated blood-perfused sino-atrial node preparation of the dog. *Tohoku, J. Exp. Med.* **121**, 383–390.

154. Sathananthan, A. H. & Burnstock, G. (1976). Evidence for a non-cholinergic, non-aminergic innervation of the venus clam heart. *Comp. Biochem. Physiol.* **55C**, 111–118.

155. Turpin, B. P., Duckworth, W. C. & Solomon, S. S. (1977). Perifusion of isolated rat adipose cells. Modulation of lipolysis by adenosine. *J. Clin. Invest.* **60**, 442–488.

156. Fain, J. N. & Wieser, P. B. (1975). Effects of adenosine deaminase on cyclic adenosine monophosphate accumulation, lipolysis, and glucose metabolism of fat cells. *J. Biol. Chem.* **250**, 1027–1034.

157. Fain, J. N. (1973). Biochemical aspects of drug and hormone action on adipose tissue. *Pharmacol. Rev.* **25**, 67–118.

158. Hynie, S. & Wenke, M. (1975). The absence of stimulation of lipolysis by papaverine, a strong inhibitor of phosphodiesterase. *Eur. J. Pharmacol.* **30**, 230–237.

159. Stock, K. & Prilop, M. (1974). Dissociation of catecholamine-induced formation of adenosine 3',5'-monophosphate and release of glycerol in fat cells by prostaglandin E_1, E_2 and N^6-phenylisopropyladenosine. *Naunym-Schmiedeberg's Arch. Pharmacol.* **282**, 15–31.

160. Schwabe, U., Schönhöfer, P. S. & Ebert, R. (1974). Facilitation by adenosine of the action of insulin on the accumulation of adenosine 3':5'-monophosphate, lipolysis, and glucose oxidation in isolated fat cells. *Eur. J. Biochem.* **46**, 537–545.

161. Hjemdahl, P. & Fredholm, B. B. (1976). Cyclic AMP-dependent and independent inhibition of lipolysis by adenosine and decreased pH. *Acta Physiol. Scand.* **96**, 170–179.

162. Born, G. V. R., Haslam, R. J. & Goldman, M. (1965). Comparative effectiveness of adenosine analogues as inhibitors of blood-platelet aggregation and as vasodilators in man. *Nature (London)* **205**, 678–680.

163. Philp, R. B., Francey, I. & McElroy, F. (1973). Effects of dipyridamole and five related agents on human platelet aggregation and adenosine uptake. *Thromb. Res.* **3**, 35–50.

164. Emmons, P. R., Harrison, M. J. G., Honour, A. J. & Mitchell, J. R. A. (1965). Effect of dipyridamole on human platelet behaviour. *Lancet* **2**, 603–606.

165. Sullivan, J. M., Harken, D. E. & Gorlin, R. (1971). Pharmacologic control of thromboembolic complications of cardiac-valve replacement. *New. Engl. J. Med.* **284**, 1391–1394.

166. Coeugniet, E. (1976). Drugs with antithrombitic effect: experimental study. *Thromb. Haemostas (Stuttg.)* **35**, 495–499.

167. Van der Weyden, M. B. & Kelley, W. N. (1976). Adenosine deaminase and immune function. *Br. J. Haematol.* **34**, 159–165.
168. Schooley, J. C. & Mahlmann, L.-J. (1975). Adenosine, AMP, cyclic AMP, theophylline and the action and production of erythropoietin. *Proc. Soc. Exp. Biol. Med.* **150**, 215–219.
169. Smyth, J. F. & Harrap, K. R. (1975). Adenosine deaminase activity in leukaemia. *Br. J. Cancer.* **31**, 544–549.
170. Van der Weyden, M. B. & Kelley, W. N. (1977). Adenosine deaminase deficiency and severe combined immunodeficiency disease. *Life Sci.* **20**, 1645–1650.
171. Chagoya de Sánchez, V., Grau, P. A., Jiménez, B., Viblalobos, R. & Piña, E. (1977). Regulation of fatty acid oxidation by adenosine at the level of its extra-mitochondrial activation. *Biochem. Biophys. Res. Commun.* **76**, 804–812.
172. Lund, P., Cornell, N. W. & Krebs, H. A. (1975). Effect of adenosine on the adenine nucleotide content and metabolism of hepatocytes. *Biochem. J.* **152**, 593–599.
173. Harris, R. A. & Yount, R. A. (1975). Inhibition of hepatic lipogenesis by adenine nucleotides. *Lipids* **10**, 673–680.
174. Kowal, J. & Fiedler, R. P. (1969). Adrenal cells in tissue culture. II: Steroidogenic responses to nucleosides and nucleotides. *Endocrinology* **84**, 1113–1117.
175. Formento, M. L., Borsa, M. & Zoni, G. (1975). Steroidogenic effect of adenosine in the rat. *Pharmacol. Res. Commun.* **7**, 247–257.
176. Ismail, N. A., El Denshary, E.-E. S. M. & Montague, W. (1977). Adenosine and the regulation of insulin secretion by isolated rat islets of Langerhans. *Biochem. J.* **164**, 409–413.
177. Gabrio, B. W., Donohue, D. M. & Finch, C. A. (1955). Erythrocyte preservation. V. Relationship between chemical changes and viability of stored blood treated with adenosine. *J. Clin. Invest.* **34**, 1509–1512.
178. De Jong, J. W. (1972). Phosphorylation and deamination of adenosine by the isolated, perfused rat heart. *Biochim. Biophys. Acta* **286**, 252–259.
179. Nordeen, S. K. & Young, D. A. (1977). Separation of effects of adenosine on energy metabolism from those on cyclic AMP in rat thymic lymphocytes. *J. Biol. Chem.* **252**, 5324–5331.
180. Sattin, A. & Rall, T. W. (1970). The effect of adenosine and adenine nucleotides on the cyclic adenosine 3′,5′-phosphate content of guinea pig cerebral cortex slices. *Mol. Pharmacol.* **6**, 13–23.
181. Daly, J. W. (1976). The nature of receptors regulating the formation of cyclic AMP in brain tissue. *Life Sci.* **18**, 1349–1358.
182. Roch, P. & Salamin, A. (1976). Adenosine promoted accumulation of adenosine 3′,5′-monophosphate in rabbit vagus nerve. *Experientia* **32**, 1419–1421.
183. Green, R. D. & Stanberry, L. R. (1977). Elevation of cyclic AMP in C-1300 murine neuroblastoma by adenosine and related compounds and the antagonism of the response by methylxanthines. *Biochem. Pharmacol.* **26**, 37–43.
184. Mills, D. C. B. & Smith, J. B. (1971). The influence on platelet aggregation of drugs that affect the accumulation of adenosine 3′:5′-cyclic monophosphate in platelets. *Biochem. J.* **121**, 185–196.
185. Wolberg, G., Zimmerman, T. P., Hiemstra, K., Winston, M. & Chu, L-C. (1975). Adenosine inhibition of lymphocyte-mediated cytolysis: possible role of cyclic adenosine monophosphate. *Science* **187**, 957–959.

186. Huang, M. & Drummond, G. I. (1976). Effect of adenosine on cyclic AMP accumulation in ventricular myocardium. *Biochem. Pharmacol.* **25**, 2713–2719.

187. Iizuka, H., Adachi, K., Halprin, K. M. & Levine, V. (1976). Adenosine and adenine nucleotides stimulation of skin (epidermal) adenylate cyclase. *Biochim. Biophys. Acta* **444**, 685–693.

188. Herlihy, J. T., Bockman, E. L., Berne, R. M. & Rubio, R. (1976). Adenosine relaxation of isolated smooth muscle. *Amer. J. Physiol.* **230**, 1239–1243.

189. Haslam, R. J. & Lynham, J. A. (1972). Activation and inhibition of blood platelet adenylate cyclase by adenosine or by 2-chloroadenosine. *Life Sci.* **11**, *Part II*, 1143–1154.

190. Clark, R. B. & Seney, M. N. (1976). Regulation of adenylate cyclase from cultured human cell lines by adenosine. *J. Biol. Chem.* **251**, 4239–4246.

191. Prémont, J., Perez, M. & Bockaert, J. (1977). Adenosine-sensitive adenylate cyclase in rat striatal homogenates and its relationship to dopamine- and Ca^{2+}-sensitive adenylate cyclases. *Mol. Pharmacol.* **13**, 662–670.

192. Haslam, R. J. & Rosson, G. M. (1975). Effects of adenosine on levels of adenosine cyclic 3′,5′-monophosphate in human blood platelets in relation to adenosine incorporation and platelet aggregation. *Mol. Pharmacol.* **11**, 528–544.

193. Shimizu, H. & Yamamura, Y. (1977). Effects of diaminopropionate, deoxyadenosine, and theophylline on stimulated formation of cyclic AMP and GMP by depolarizing agents in slices of guinea-pig cerebral cortex. *J. Neurochem.* **28**, 383–388.

194. Olsson, R. A., Davis, C. J., Khouri, E. M. & Patterson, R. E. (1976). Evidence for an adenosine receptor on the surface of dog coronary myocytes. *Circ. Res.* **39**, 93–98.

195. Saito, M. (1977). Elevation of guanosine 3′,5′-monophosphate level by adenosine in cerebellar slices of guinea pig. *Biochim. Biophys. Acta* **498**, 316–324.

196. Ohga, Y. & Daly, J. W. (1977). Calcium ion-elicited accumulations of cyclic GMP in guinea pig cerebellar slices. *Biochim. Biophys. Acta* **498**, 61–75.

197. Haslam, R. J. (1975). Roles of cyclic nucleotides in platelet function. *Ciba Found. Symp.* **35**, 121–151.

198. Verhaeghe, R. H. (1977). Action of adenosine and adenine nucleotides on dogs' isolated veins. *Amer. J. Physiol.* **233**, H114–H121.

Subject Index